SOLAR HEATING

WILLIAM G. SCHELLER

Howard W. Sams & Co., Inc.
4300 WEST 62ND ST. INDIANAPOLIS, INDIANA 46268 USA

FIRST EDITION
FIRST PRINTING—1980

International Standard Book Number: 0-672-21621-3
Library of Congress Catalog Card Number: 80-50049

Printed in the United States of America.

PREFACE

Necessity is the mother of invention. When people think about solar energy, it often appears to them to be an "invention" brought into being in answer to the "necessity" created by the energy shortage with which we have lived for the past seven years. But the idea of harnessing the sun to do our work goes back a great deal further than the nineteen seventies —just as the inevitable prospect of fossil fuel shortages goes back further than the Arab oil embargo. Neither the invention nor the necessity are all that new.

Most of the solar applications that are attracting such interest today are refinements of ideas that have been around for centuries, and, in the case of passive solar heating and cooling, for thousands of years. But this would-be technology was allowed to languish during our industrial age, when cheap oil, coal, and gas became so universally available that even people who should have known better acted as if it all came from some inexhaustible supply. In a study of United States energy options commissioned in the early 1950s, it was concluded that solar power was a reasonable alternative, one that could be developed to play a major role in the nation's energy economy within four or five years. But these recommendations went unheeded, and we sped on toward our current predicament. Now people suddenly recall that there were reliable solar water heaters in parts of the country at the turn of the century, and that the 1933 Chicago World's Fair featured a house that got a large part of its heat from big, south-facing windows. People "remember" things they had known all along, such as how hot a closed automobile gets on a bright winter day. All of this remembrance has added up to a rediscovery of solar energy. It may not exactly be invention; there is no denying the necessity.

William G. Scheller

PREFACE

CONTENTS

CHAPTER 1

INTRODUCTION 7

CHAPTER 2

HOW SUNLIGHT BEHAVES 11

CHAPTER 3

INSULATION: CONSERVING HEAT FROM THE SUN
(OR FROM ANY SOURCE) 19

CHAPTER 4

LIQUID FLAT-PLATE COLLECTORS: THE BASIC
SOLAR HARDWARE 23

CHAPTER 5

THE DOMESTIC HOT WATER SYSTEM 35

CHAPTER 6

SOLAR SPACE HEATING 53

CHAPTER 6

SOLAR SPACE HEATING 53

CHAPTER 7

PAYBACK 89

CHAPTER 8

SOLAR HEATING OF A SWIMMING POOL 95

CHAPTER 9

SOLAR COOLING 103

APPENDIX A

CALCULATING HEAT LOAD 139

APPENDIX B

SOLAR MANUFACTURERS 141

APPENDIX C

MEAN PERCENTAGE OF POSSIBLE SUNSHINE FOR SELECTED LOCATIONS 145

GLOSSARY 149

INDEX 157

Chapter 1

INTRODUCTION

It is most frustrating these days, having spent time around solar heating system users and installers, having watched temperatures rise in solar water storage tanks even on cloudy days, having read accounts of wonderful successes with experimental solar buildings, to then run into someone who says, "Oh, solar energy—do you think anything will come of that?" Or, "Yes, solar. I guess they'll get that perfected someday." Perhaps the most common variation is simply, "Does it really work?"

Something has come of it. Certain facets of solar technology—among them some of the most practical and immediately useful for the homeowner—have been perfected quite nicely. And yes, it really does work.

Perhaps the skepticism is understandable. As old as the principles behind man's use of solar energy are, the claims sometimes seem a little too good to be true, and the hardware so simple that it surely must be deceptive. But it is all based on sound facts about heat transfer and retention, sound plumbing and air distribution, and a sound understanding of the earth's position in space as a huge solar collector.

Consider the following examples:

1. An architect builds a three-story home with 2,200 feet of floor space in northern Idaho—hardly a place known for mild winters. The south slope of his roof, which is in complete harmony with the rest of the building, resembles a massive, sectioned skylight. However, air blown through channels beneath that glazing provides the home with 72 percent of its annual space heating and domestic hot water requirements. The system cost $7500; it will have paid for itself in seven years.

2. A ranch house on a residential street in Peabody, Massachusetts, looks no different, from the front, than its neighbors. However, there is an array of four solar collectors on the south-facing roof that projects from the rear. Four gallons of nontoxic antifreeze liquid flows

through these collectors and into an exchange coil, which in turn heats the home water supply in a 120-gallon basement tank. The owner's water heating bills will be 60 to 80 percent of what they were before the collectors were installed. The cost of the system, including tax credits and a $400 HUD grant available at the time, was less than $2,000.

3. A house in Wyoming is built without any pumps, blowers, or other mechanical devices to circulate solar-heated air or water. But its orientation toward the sun, along with the architect's careful use of glass and solid masonry masses, assures an indoor temperature 50 to 60°F higher than that of the outdoors during periods of 0°F weather —*without* assistance from auxiliary heating systems. The owner then uses the auxiliary heating system (in this case a pair of wood stoves) to bring the indoor temperature up a mere 10 to 15 degrees. Imagine how much less this costs than if the home were heated only by conventional means.

These are three very different examples of solar-heated buildings. In the Wyoming house, it is true that intrinsic design plays a major role in the efficiency with which the sun's energy is put to use. The Massachusetts house had never been designed as a "solar" dwelling; but its unobstructed south-facing roof was all that was needed for collectors to be installed successfully. Had a larger surface been available, extra collectors could have helped play a part in space heating, as they do in the Idaho residence. These three houses show how much or how little solar utilization can be a function of design, and they also demonstrate the extreme diversity and versatility of solar technology even at this early stage of its development. In one or another of its forms solar energy has a rightful and practical place in the plans of the vast majority of people who are planning to build or renovate a home, or who are simply tired of the relentless climb of fuel and utility rates. And even the more exotic, experimental applications—such as solar air conditioning and photovoltaic generation of electricity—deserve our attention and enthusiasm. Otherwise, when thousands of others are enjoying the benefits, we will still be wondering if they "really work."

ACTIVE AND PASSIVE SOLAR SYSTEMS

The means which have been devised for making use of the sun's energy are generally referred to as either "passive" or "active"—thus the terms "passive solar house" or "active solar house." (A house incorporating elements from both sets of principles is said to be a "hybrid.")

Passive solar technology (Fig. 1.1) is largely a branch of architec-

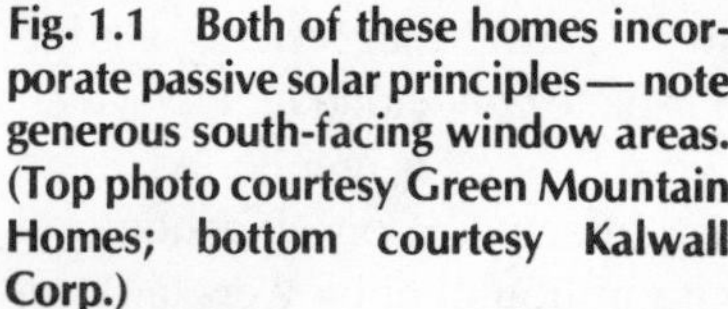

Fig. 1.1 Both of these homes incorporate passive solar principles — note generous south-facing window areas. (Top photo courtesy Green Mountain Homes; bottom courtesy Kalwall Corp.)

ture, even though it has taken many architects quite a while to rediscover some basic concepts which were foolishly discarded during our ill-fated fling with cheap fossil fuels. Aeschylus, the Greek dramatist, wrote 2500 years ago that one of the things which separated barbarians from civilized people was that the latter had houses that "turned towards the sun." Several hundred years later, the Roman architect Vitruvius argued that "we must design houses according to climate." He advised the clustering of living areas around the warmer, southern exposures of a house. Many of antiquity's better ideas were picked up and dusted off after the Middle Ages, but this one remained a mystery to even our better-educated builders until solar advocates began to "see the light" in our own century.

As we will learn in a more detailed look at passive solar heating and cooling further on in this book, not every application of the passive solar principles requires that the owner start at the drawing board. There are a number of passive design features which can be incorporated into standing homes; the solar greenhouse is the most outstanding example. Some people may even discover ways of using the passive solar elements that have been thwarted or simply ignored in the homes in which they have been living. However, the total passive solar system must be built into the house. More precisely, the house itself is the system.

Most people are more familiar with the active solar systems; it is the skylight shape and appearance of the flat-plate collector (Fig. 1.2) which most often comes to mind when the word "solar" is mentioned. In an active system, energy from the sun is collected at one location and distributed to where it is needed by pumps (liquid) or blowers (air). An active solar system, then, relies on external sources of power to operate the machinery with which it circulates heat through collectors and into a storage facility, and then to where it is required in the home. Of course, much less energy is used to operate these simple circulating devices than would be consumed by conventional heating equipment. It is this advantage, combined with the efficiency of the collectors themselves, that assures that the installation will pay for itself in energy savings. This is what solar researchers and manufacturers refer to as "payback." The "payback period" is the time it takes a solar system to save its owner a sum equivalent to the cost of purchasing and installing the system.

There is a great deal to learn about the various solar systems available: how the individual components work, what the most efficient modes of installation are, and how to determine, plan, and shop for the equipment or design that will work best in a present or future home. Before examining the hardware, let us review some of the basic facts about the sun's energy and how it is collected on earth.

Fig. 1.2 These houses are equipped with active solar collectors. Thirteen collectors in left picture provide both space heat and hot water; smaller array on right picture is for hot water only. (Left photo courtesy Grumman Corp.; right courtesy Solar Solutions/Peter Southwick, photographer.)

Chapter 2

HOW SUNLIGHT BEHAVES

We referred earlier to the earth itself as an enormous "solar collector." This definition will seem obvious to anyone who notices that it gets light in the morning, or warm in the summer. But there is more to an understanding of solar energy than the appreciation of day and night, or hot and cold. The sun does not simply radiate warmth and light to the earth; it produces the energy that, under our atmospheric conditions, is received in the form of warmth and light.

The sun is a vast thermonuclear furnace in which hydrogen atoms fuse to produce helium. The temperature reached in this furnace—25 million degrees Fahrenheit at the core, 10,000°F at the surface—should make us thankful for our 93 million mile distance from the sun. The energy represented by these intense solar temperatures crosses this gulf of space in the form of radiation traveling in an assortment of wavelengths. Almost half of the energy radiated by the sun travels in the infrared wavelengths, that is, at a frequency just below that of the visible light which we perceive as the color red. It is this form of radiation which we feel as heat. Another 46 percent of solar energy reaches us in the wavelengths which make up the visible spectrum; ultraviolet light accounts for the remainder. The radiation of the visible and infrared wavelengths is absorbed and turned into heat energy within the active collector devices and passively heated homes (Fig. 2.1). It is the availability throughout the year of this type of radiation that makes the solar collector efficient in winter as well as summer.

There are other factors that affect the amount of solar radiation that can be collected on earth. One is the planet's atmosphere. Another is its orbital position and axis rotation, or in more familiar terms, the season of the year and the time of day.

Everyone has observed that althouh it is impossible to look safely at the sun when it is directly overhead, it is not difficult to face west, eyes

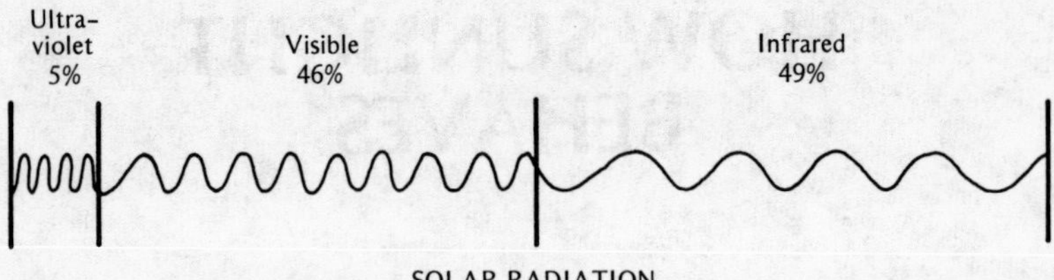

Fig. 2.1 Solar collectors make use of the energy in the visible and infrared portions of the sun's spectrum.

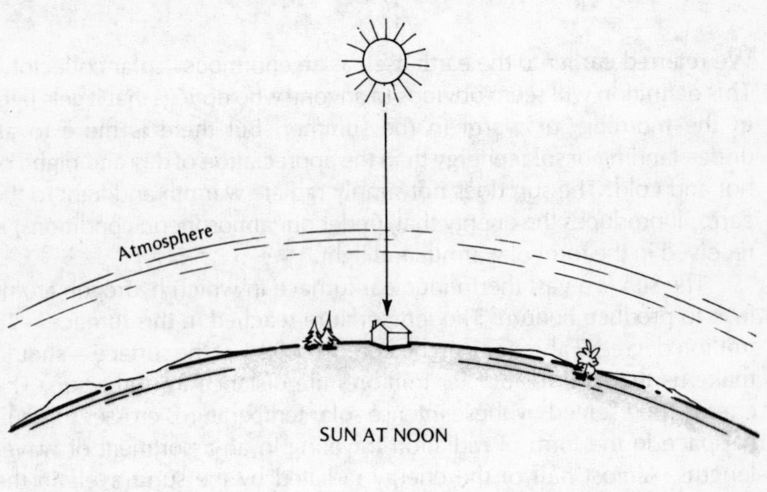

Fig. 2.2 Solar radiation is much more intense towards middle of day, when it receives less atmospheric interference.

wide open, and enjoy the sunset. This is because there is a great difference in the amount of interference that the sun's rays encounter in the atmosphere at different times of the day. When the sun is overhead, as at noon or one o'clock, its rays are able to take the most direct route through the layers of air, water vapor, and particulate matter that surround the earth. This minimum amount of interference results in strong, intense sunlight and an image of the sun too bright for our eyes to tolerate. (See Fig. 2.2.) Early or late in the day, however, these same rays must glance horizontally through a much thicker layer of atmosphere, and the result is weaker rays. Our eyes can take this light and safely turn it into a picture of the rising or setting sun. This is how the atmosphere, helped by the earth's rotation on its axis, creates the visual phenomena of dusk and daybreak.

The atmosphere also scatters the solar energy as it is approaching the planet's surface. A significant portion of the sun's energy does not even reach the point where it can be absorbed, scattered, or directly radiated to the earth's surface. As much as 35 percent of sunlight is simply reflected back into space. Yet another 10 to 15 percent is absorbed, either by ozone in the upper atmosphere or by water vapor and carbon dioxide farther below, before reaching the planet's surface. (See Fig. 2.3.)

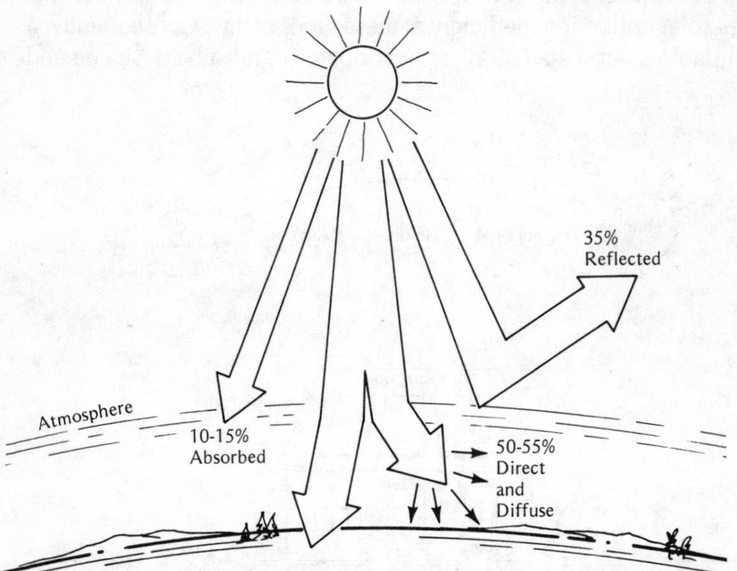

Fig. 2.3 Not all solar radiation is received directly by the earth's surface.

Fifty percent, then, of the solar radiation directed at the earth does in fact pass through the atmosphere to the surface, but only a part reaches us directly. The remainder takes the form of *diffuse* radiation—that is, rays that have been scattered upon contact with air molecules, moisture, and atmospheric dust. It is this diffuse sunlight which is responsible for the blue to gray color of the sky on most days. Although diffuse radiation is not as intense as direct solar radiation and appears to come from no specific source, it is nevertheless useful as a source of heat energy. People who are skeptical of solar heating often ask, "What about overcast days?" The answer is that diffuse solar radiation is absorbed and collected as heat by the same devices that garner warmth from direct rays. For proof, visit a home with solar space heating or a domestic hot water system on a hazy day. You will notice that the temperature of the solar transfer fluid still exceeds that of the atmosphere or of unheated tapwater. Later, in the chapters describing the construction and operation of flat-plate collectors and other solar hardware, we will take a closer look at the means by which diffuse (and direct) radiation is put to work.

The turning of the earth on its axis also affects our ability to make use of solar energy. As was noted previously, the horizontal rays of early morning and late afternoon must travel through a broad measure of atmosphere. But it is also the angle of the rays themselves that makes solar collection inefficient at these times of day. Consequently, a dependable solar installation, active or passive, must be designed and

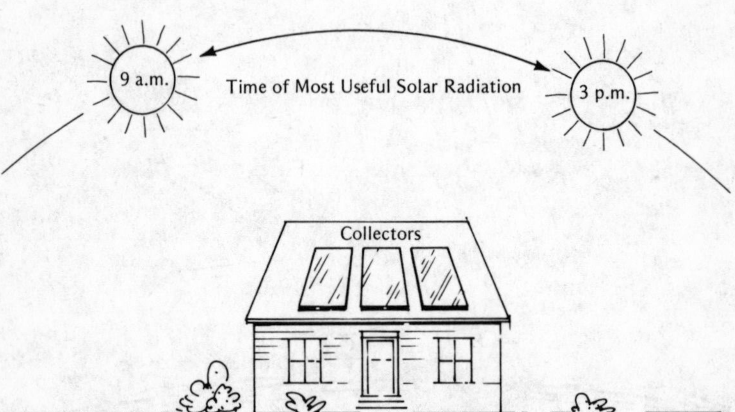

Fig. 2.4 Collectors must be situated so that they can make use of the solar radiation occurring between the hours of 9 and 3 each day.

constructed to make use of the radiation that occurs between the hours of 9:00 A.M. and 3:00 P.M. each day. (See Fig. 2.4.)

This leads to another question commonly asked of solar enthusiasts, "What if I want to take a shower at night?" Darkness cannot be avoided; that is why you have a well insulated 80 to 120 gallon tank as a part of your solar domestic hot water installation, and an even larger storage facility if the system is used for space heating as well. (Incidentally, if the temperature of the water in the storage tank has fallen sufficiently due to heavy use and the introduction of cold water from an outside supply, it is not unusual for collectors in domestic hot water systems to continue circulating fluid and absorbing heat after dark on hot summer nights.)

The change of seasons caused by the earth's tilt on its axis and its path of orbit around the sun must also be considered. The farther north or south you travel from the equator into the temperate zones, the more pronounced the difference between winter and summer. This is not because there is any significant change in the distance between the earth and sun as it completes each orbit, but rather because the planet's axis has a constant 23½ degree tilt from the vertical. Because of this tilt, the northern hemisphere is inclined more directly toward the sun in the summer but slants away from the sun in winter. This yearly change affects the angle at which rays of sunlight strike the surfaces of the globe. During winter, sunlight glances through a greater amount of the earth's atmosphere, and those of us who live in the temperate zone north of the equator say that the sun is "lower" in the sky. Meanwhile, of course, the southern hemisphere is receiving solar radiation at an angle much closer to the perpendicular.

Therefore when solar energy is to be collected and used, designers and builders must consider first what function the installation is to perform, and then take into account the latitude at which it will be located. (See Fig. 2.5.) If flat-plate collectors are to be used to activate an air-conditioning system, they must be placed on an angle at which they will be most receptive to the summer sun. For a space-heating system, collectors must gather as much energy as they can from slanting winter rays; this dictates a steeper angle, in addition to the mandatory southern orientation. What about latitude? The optimum slant for a collector array in a Florida domestic hot water system will not apply in Montreal; the rays of the winter sun are more direct in the southerly location. If we were to use extremes as an example, we might imagine a nearly vertical collector in the high arctic, and one set almost parallel to the ground at the equator.

Passive design as well is based upon awareness of the angles at which solar radiation strikes an area in different seasons. Sunlight in a

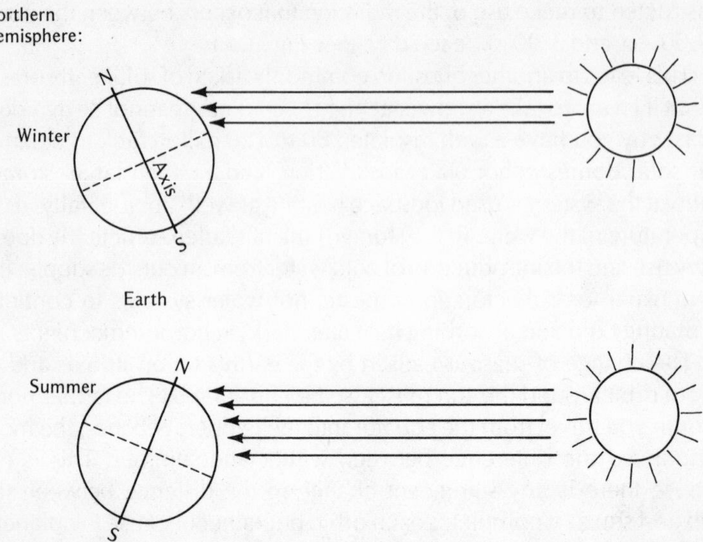

Fig. 2.5 Angle of earth towards sun differs with the seasons. Collectors must be tilted according to their primary time of usefulness; if they serve a year-round function, a compromise may be reached.

south-facing window may be welcome in the winter, but in June, the inhabitants of a house designed with such a feature will want an overhang to shade the glass from the high summer sun. (The importance of two calculations—those of solar *altitude* and *azimuth*—in passive design will be discussed in Chapter 10.)

INSOLATION AND SUNSHINE PERCENTAGE

Compilations of climactic data have led to rough measurements of the amount and quality of sunshine which can be expected under average conditions in different geographic locations. These measurements are given in terms of *insolation* and *percentage of possible sunshine*.

"Insolation" is a condensed form for the term "incident solar radiation." Although it is shorter and more convenient than the original phrase, it can cause problems when it is confused with insulation—another, more familiar term that also figures into any thorough discussion of solar energy. Insolation refers to the amount of solar radiation that falls during a specific period on a given surface at a particular latitude. All incident radiation is included, diffuse as well as direct, and even that reflected from surfaces such as sand or snow.

Insolation measurements are given in "langleys." A langley is one calorie of radiant energy per square centimeter, or 3.69 Btu per square foot. The period of time over which incident radiation is recorded is usually one day. The insolation data available from the American Society of Heating, Refrigerating, and Air-Conditioning Engineers (ASHRAE) is based on the radiation received on surfaces placed at various angles to the sun. This data can help determine such variables as the best angle for solar collectors.

The other measurement used to record the availability of solar energy is the "percentage of possible sunshine." This is the percentage of time that sunlight is strong enough to cause an object in its path to cast a shadow. The figure is defined for each specific area over the course of a year, and assumes typical weather conditions for that area during that year. For possible sunshine percentage data, see Appendix C at the end of this book.

Do not be discouraged if after consulting maps and charts for your area, you find what seem to be low insolation and low possible sunshine figures. Some areas of North America are better suited for solar energy than others. The Southwest, with its clear, cold winter days, is at the 80th to 90th percentile of possible sunshine and is an ideal location for active solar space heating systems. But solar domestic hot water installations —and an increasing number of space heating setups—are performing quite well for homeowners across the continent, even in places like northern New England and the Pacific Northwest that are in the 40 to 50 possible sunshine percentile. Remember, a solar system does not have to function at top efficiency 100 percent of the time in order to save you money on oil, gas, or electricity. A passively heated or cooled home is an energy saver in any climate. The earth itself receives only two billionths of the sun's total output of radiant energy; still, things have been growing nicely here for years.

Chapter 3

INSULATION: CONSERVING HEAT FROM THE SUN (OR FROM ANY SOURCE)

In the last chapter, we saw how energy from the sun reaches the earth and comes into contact with the devices designed to make use of it. Before detailing the operation of these devices, it would be a good idea to consider how heat behaves *after* it has been collected and put to work to make living spaces comfortable. This is where insulation (with a "u," this time) comes into play.

Heat always flows from a warmer to a cooler body. In the case of a house, this means that warmth contained within the structure's walls and roof seeks to pass through these surfaces into the cooler outside environment. (See Fig. 3.1.) In the summer, the same principle is at work

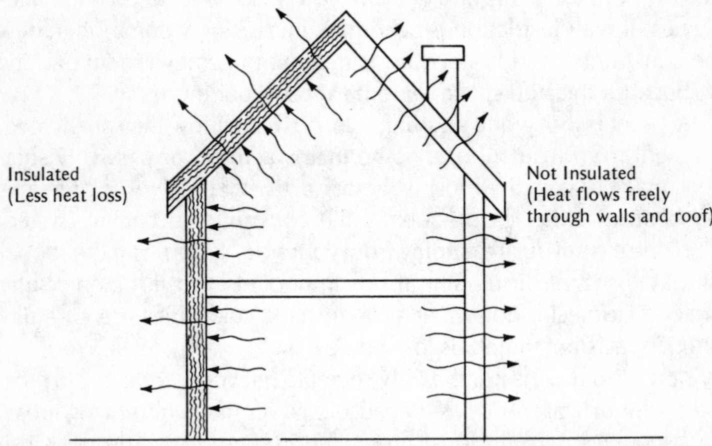

Fig. 3.1 Good insulation blocks wasteful heat flow, and is important regardless of whether a home is heated by solar or conventional means.

in reverse: heat from outdoors is constantly trying to penetrate the house's shell in order to warm the interior. Assuming that energy—solar or otherwise—is being expended in order to keep the living area warm or cool, it makes sense to put up as much resistance as possible to the flow of heat.

Resistance is what insulation is all about. The R value (R for resistance) is the term used in measuring a material's insulating capacity. A vacuum is the ideal insulator; since vacuums are not attainable within the walls or roofs of buildings, we must instead rely on dead air trapped within insulating materials to block the conduction of heat. Fiberglass batting is one example of such a material. Its spun fibers create millions of pockets in which air does not move and thus cannot carry heat away through the motion of its molecules. Shredded cellulose (blown into the stud spaces of buildings that have interior walls in place), mineral wool (also blown into walls and attic floors), and rigid polystyrene are all materials that insulate because they contain pockets of trapped air.

This is not the place to go into the choice of insulation materials and the amount of insulation recommended for different climates, except to note that the more insulation (i.e., the higher the R value) in the walls, attic, and first floors or basement of a house, the more heat will be conserved. Obviously there is a point of diminishing returns, and this point is linked to the cost of heating, the cost of insulation, and the space available for the installation of insulating materials. The figures of four inches for walls and six to nine inches for attics are often mentioned. If fiberglass batting were the insulation chosen, this would mean approximately R-14 in the walls and R-21 to R-31 in the attic. In cold climates six inches of wall insulation is becoming increasingly common in new house construction. This standard is difficult to achieve in an existing home because the stud space seldom exceeds four inches.

The point is that while all structures, no matter how they are heated, will benefit from insulation, a home that is actively or passively solar heated stands to gain the most. Whether active or passive, solar heat is stored heat, and the less frequently the conventional backup system goes on, the more you are gaining from your solar system and the sooner it will pay for itself. Insulation also is important even if the only solar fixture is a domestic hot water system; tanks and pipes are carefully swathed in resistant materials to hold heat in.

Good insulation is not the only secret to heat conservation. In most houses, a lot of warmth is lost because cold air filters into living areas. This happens for two reasons: first, windows and doors do not close tightly, or doors are used which open directly into heated areas rather than into "buffer" zones like vestibules or mudrooms; and second, draft-inviting cracks and chinks have developed around foundation sills, window frames, chimneys, and other exterior locations where one surface meets another. A couple of afternoons spent with caulking guns and weather stripping will eliminate many of these problems. The importance of insulation and infiltration blockage in a house using solar energy can be summed up simply: a good house is a tight house.

Chapter 4

LIQUID FLAT-PLATE COLLECTORS: THE BASIC SOLAR HARDWARE

At the current state of solar development, it is the liquid flat-plate collector (Fig. 4.1) that enables most people to capture and make use of the sun's energy in active systems. Flat-plate collectors are the sky-

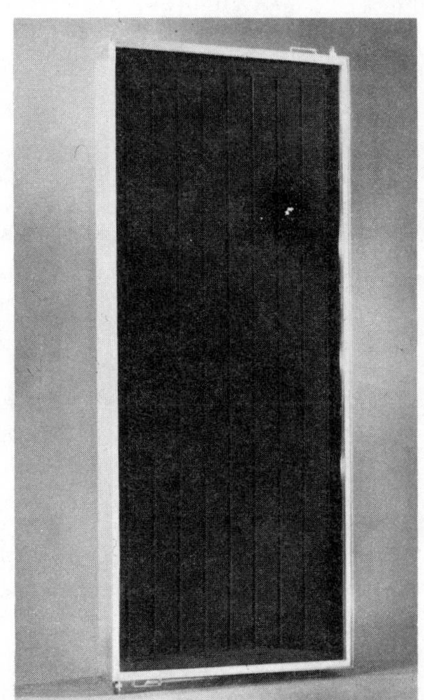

Fig. 4.1 A liquid-type flat-plate solar collector. Note tubing in absorber plate. (Courtesy Libbey-Owens-Ford.)

lightlike panels that we referred to earlier. Their popularity stems from the relative ease with which they can be installed on or adjacent to residences that may not have been originally designed to take advantage of solar energy, and from the efficiency of their conversion of the sun's radiation into heat for domestic water supplies and space heating uses.

The term "flat-plate collector" technically includes panels that supply currents of warmed air for the same purposes. Although these units trap and convert solar energy in much the same way as the liquid models, the means of heat distribution and storage which they employ is substantially different. They will be discussed in Chapter 6 of this book.

GREENHOUSE EFFECT

In order to understand how a collector works, it is first necessary to understand a few points about how it is constructed and about the behavior of sunlight as it reaches the surface of the collector. The typical flat-plate collector consists primarily of a heat-absorptive surface through which a fluid circulates and a layer of glazing placed about two inches above the absorber. (There are special-purpose exceptions, several of which we will examine later.) What happens in the space between these two components is called the *greenhouse effect* (Fig. 4.2). This effect was observed by the French scientist Nicholas de Saussure as early as the eighteenth century; he was the first to assemble a simple glazed box which could be said to be the forerunner of the modern collector. But greenhouses had been used long before Saussure's time. People today who have never heard of his work make the same observations he did when they park their cars in direct sunlight and close the windows.

When the short-frequency solar rays of the visible spectrum pass through a pane of glass, they strike whatever surface lies on the opposite side and turn into long-wave heat radiation. Although the short-frequency rays are able to make their way easily through the glass, the resulting heat cannot escape as easily. The heat is trapped within the glazed-over area—in this case, a solar collector panel—and absorbed by the surface beneath the glass. The darker the surface is, the greater the absorptive capacity. This is why the inside of a flat-plate collector is so much warmer than the air surrounding it, and why it is an efficient "harvester" of solar energy even on days when other solid surfaces appear not to have been warmed at all.

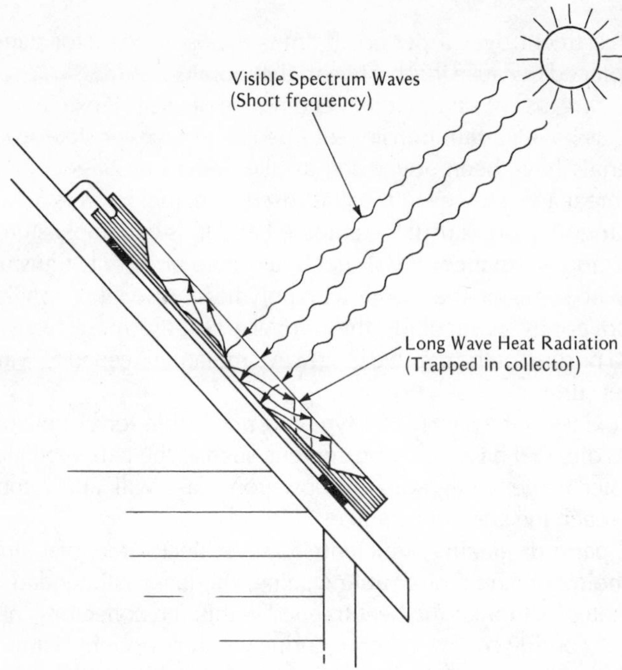

Fig. 4.2 The "greenhouse effect" is what makes flat-plate collectors efficient absorbers of solar energy.

CONSTRUCTION OF COLLECTORS

There are a great many brands and varieties of flat-plate solar collectors on the market today. Each differs somewhat from the others in design and choice of materials, as the pictures throughout this book illustrate. All collectors share enough similarities to enable us to examine the basic components of a typical model.

The *housing*, comprising the side walls and back of a collector, may be made of aluminum, steel, fiberglass, or, in some homemade installations, wood. The housing has to form a tight seal against the other components and be able to withstand constant exposure to the elements. The payback feature of a solar system—its ability to return its owner's investment over a period of time—is lost if collector panels must be replaced because this basic part deteriorates.

The *glazing*, as we saw before, need not be of glass. Plexiglass has been used, as have certain translucent fiberglass-polyester sheets. The latter materials have been advertised as alternatives to glass because they resist breakage. However, the glass used by manufacturers of high quality solar collectors is usually tempered and thus extremely sturdy. Glass is a stable substance; it will not deteriorate or lose its transmissivity, as will some of the plastics or polymers. Also, the nonglass collector coverings, particularly the thinner ones, are more likely to retransmit a portion of the captive long-wave radiation needed to warm the absorber surface.

Not all glass is the same. The type most desirable for use in solar collectors is one that has a low iron content, such as the tempered glass called "water-white." High-quality, low-iron glass will allow more sunlight to reach the absorber surface.

Is one pane of glazing sufficient? Some collector manufacturers offer the choice of single or double glazing; the latter is intended for colder climates. Although the heat trapped within the collector is held more securely during cold weather or during windy periods by a double covering of glass (or by plastic film-and-glass tandem glazing), there is a trade-off: a smaller amount of sunlight is transmitted through two panes of glass than through one. This loss of transmissivity will not usually exceed seven percent, however. The gains in collection and storage temperatures—particularly in space-heating systems—may easily offset this transmissivity reduction.

Along with the glazing, perhaps the most important feature of a flat-plate solar collector is the "absorber plate." (See Fig. 4.3.) This is the surface that absorbs the heat trapped beneath the glazing, and through which the fluid heat-exchange medium passes. As we noted before, dark surfaces make the best heat absorbers. That is why desert dwellers wear white, and why absorber plates are nearly always black.

Three factors contribute to the heat-absorbing and conduction efficiency of a collector plate. The first is the material from which the plate and its tubing are made. The second is the means by which tubes and plate are joined. Finally, there is the question of how the black surface is applied to the plate.

Although some solar experts expect plastics to play a significant part in the future manufacture of absorber plates and tubing, the choice at present is largely limited to copper, aluminum, or steel. Copper, the most expensive of the three, is nevertheless desirable because it is the

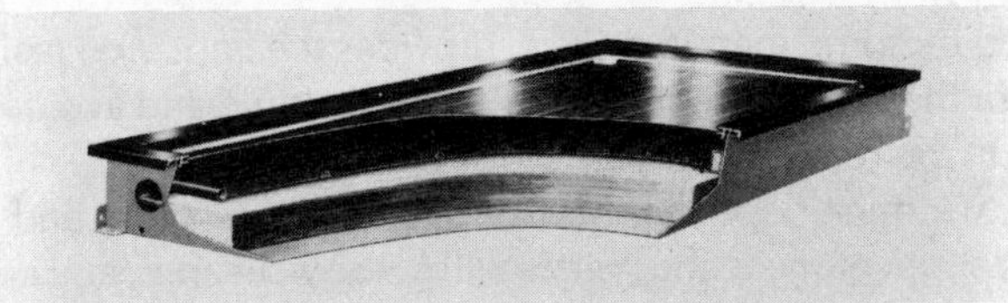

Fig. 4.3 Cutaway view of a flat-plate collector. Note heavy layer of insulation below absorber plate. (Courtesy Lennox Industries.)

least subject to corrosion when it is used for tubing through which water or a water and antifreeze mixture is to be circulated. It also has undeniable advantages as the material for the plate surfaces themselves; its excellent conductivity and lack of any tendency toward "hot spots" make thinner plates feasible. Among copper's other strong points are its light weight and the ease with which separate pieces of it can be soldered or brazed together.

The way tubes and plates are bonded also affects the collector's efficiency. Here again there is a choice. Basically, there are two options: the tubing can be an integral part of the plate or it can be secured to the plate by means of soldering or mechanical connection.

The first procedure, resulting in what is called a "tube-in-plate" (Fig. 4.4), is simply the result of laminating two channeled metal surfaces so that the channels meet to form closed passageways for the heat transfer fluid. The second method involves more intricate construction procedures. The soldering of the tubes to the plate must be done properly, or else thermal conductivity will suffer. However, the use of separate components introduces the possibility of combining copper tubing with steel or aluminum sheeting for the plates. This alternative,

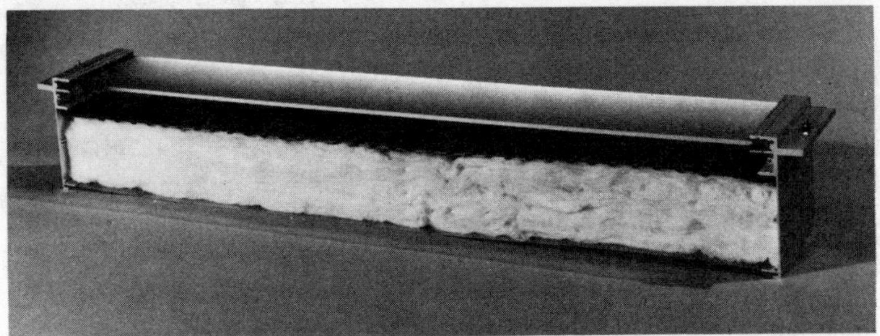

Fig. 4.4 Another cutaway view. Note tube-in-plate construction of absorber, which eliminates welding of tubing onto surface. (Courtesy Grumman Corp.)

employed by some manufacturers, provides the corrosion resistance of copper for the surfaces that actually touch the fluid and avoids copper's expense in the remainder of the unit.

Still, we must hope that new plastics prove efficient and that they take over soon. None of the metals will get any cheaper, and copper has become increasingly scarce as well.

The third efficiency factor is the black surface coating for the plate and tubing. Black paint has long been the standard in many collectors although its durability can vary. Remember, the surface of a solar absorber plate is subjected to extremely high temperatures. The better manufacturers have sought out tough, long-lasting varieties of paint or have turned to alternatives such as black chrome bonded to metal plates over an intermediate plating of nickel. One of the advantages of the chrome plating is that its textured surface absorbs up to 96 percent of the solar radiation which reaches it.

The make-up of a solar collector is completed by the gaskets that seal the housing and glass and prevent moisture entry and fogging, and by the insulation placed at the back and sides of the collector that prevents heat from escaping through opaque surfaces. The two most popular insulation materials to date are fiberglass and urethane foam. Manufacturers using fiberglass point out that foam can break down under high temperatures and that the resulting gases leave a film on the inside of the collector's glazing. Others favor foam because of its higher R value, and say that the dangers of decomposition are exaggerated. One precautionary construction method is to insulate with foam, and cover the material with a plastic film that will prevent any gas leakage that might occur.

A Variation on Flat-Plate Collector Design

The unit described above (and its slight variations) has been accepted as the standard flat-plate collector design. There have been, however, several innovations which depart significantly from the basic format. One of the more interesting is SolaRoll™, a flexible heat-absorbing and fluid-circulating mat invented by Michael Zinn and Steven Krulick and sold by Bio-energy Systems of Spring Glen, New York. SolaRoll™ (Fig. 4.5) is expressly designed for on-site fabrication of solar collectors. It consists of two components: the mat itself and a framing strip to hold the glazing above the collector surface. Both are made of a long-lasting synthetic rubber. The manufacturers of this product feel that its advantages lie in portability and ease of installation: once insulation and

Fig. 4.5 SolaRoll™ flexible absorber mats. Lower photo shows house with these mats installed and glazed. Note home's passive design features. (Courtesy Bio-Energy Systems, Inc.)

backing have been applied to a surface, the mats are secured with a cartridge-held adhesive. Water flows through hollow tubing in the mat and is routed to storage through copper header pipes. The glazing is usually a thin layer of polyester-reinforced fiberglass.

The synthetic rubber collector mat has a lower thermal conductivity than copper or aluminum. Its inventors feel that this disadvantage is effectively countered by the relatively high amount of heat energy per dollar that their system delivers.

PLANNING THE LOCATION OF FLAT-PLATE COLLECTORS

Before heading indoors to trace the details of how fluid circulated through a solar collector provides a home's hot water or heats the living areas, we should take a close look at how flat-plate panels are effectively positioned.

In Chapter 2, we saw that the angling of collectors has a great deal to do with the latitude at which the installation is made. The farther north you go (in the Northern Hemisphere), the steeper the angle a collector array requires in order to be efficient year round. A qualified solar installer will be able to calculate the proper collector angle for a given location, as well as to subtract from it the angle already created by the roof to which the collectors are to be attached. Even if you purchase a system for do-it-yourself installation, it is wise to have the seller visit your site and recommend the best angle. Most suppliers of solar equipment will provide this service to do-it-yourselfers, and some will even include it in the system's purchase price.

There is, however, an easy rule of thumb for roughly calculating the angle at which to raise a solar collector from the horizontal. (See Fig. 4.6.) Start with the latitude at which your site is located. If your solar system is to be used year-round to heat home water supplies, with perhaps some winter space heating also expected of it, the angle of tilt should roughly correspond to the latitude of the site. If your main objective is heating in the winter, add 15 degrees to the latitude figure; in other words, tilt the collector more towards the vertical. If the system is designed primarily for summer collection (i.e., for air conditioning in an area where that mode of operation is practical), subtract 15 degrees from your latitude. Remember, the sun is higher overhead in summer, and higher also as you approach the equator. Therefore the solar collectors will be closer to the horizontal the closer you are to the equator; this also holds true if you are using the collectors for air conditioning.

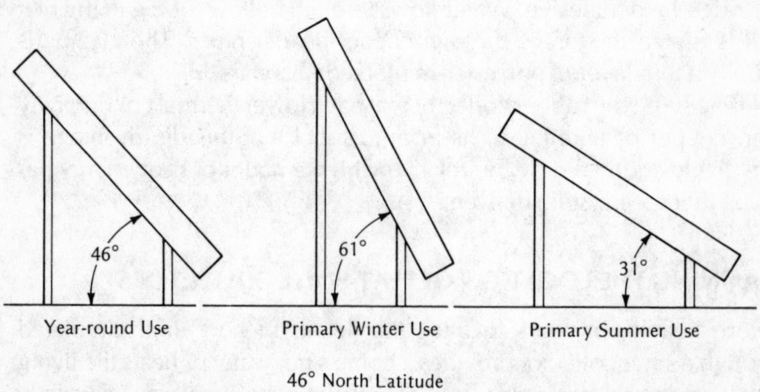

Fig. 4.6 Diagram shows how collector tilt conforms to angle of sunlight during season of peak use.

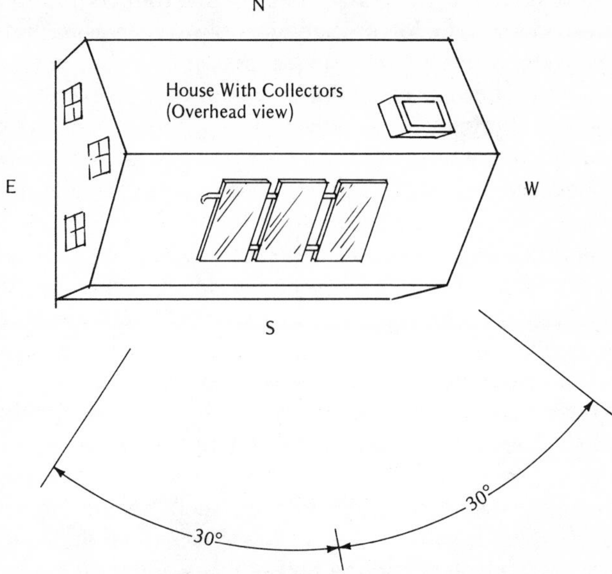

ACCEPTABLE ORIENTATION FOR SOLAR COLLECTORS

Fig. 4.7 Acceptable deviation from true south in orientation of collectors.

Along with angling, the most important factor in the positioning of collectors is *orientation*. Orientation is the compass direction an array of the panels faces. In the Northern Hemisphere south is the direction from which we can receive the most sunlight, especially during the winter.

Some homeowners who cannot manage a perfectly southerly collector orientation on their site despair of obtaining maximum benefit from solar energy. Actually they need not worry as long as the deviation is not excessive. Tests have shown that if the collector orientation varies no more than 30 degrees in either direction from true south, loss of efficiency is only marginal (Fig. 4.7). Bruce Anderson and Michael Riordan, authors of *The Solar Home Book,* even suggest that some situations might dictate a deliberate deviation. They advise that turning the collectors slightly (perhaps 10 degrees) to the west could make the system the beneficiary of higher afternoon temperatures. A similar alteration in the opposite direction could help at sites where afternoon cloudiness is prevalent. In short, the idea is to tailor the installation for the climatic variations that can most reasonably be expected.

If an orientation within 30 degrees of true south is not feasible, it is possible to make up for lost efficiency simply by increasing the total area of the collector array. But the "simply" lies in the doing, not necessarily in the paying. Unless you are building collectors on-site for a minimal cost, or unless money is no object, it seems foolish to add collector surface if the orientation begins to approach true east or true west. And beyond these points no increase in collector area can recoup efficiency loss.

If an acceptable roof top orientation is not possible, it is better to look around for installation opportunities other than on the roof of the main building. Many collector arrays have been successfully mounted at ground level. Nearby outbuildings are also a possible installation site. You may have a north-south orientation to the roofline of your house with the sloping sides facing east and west. However, perhaps your garage, shed, or another adjacent structure faces in a more desirable direction.

The one potential difficulty with any such "remote" installation is the possibility of heat being lost by the transfer fluid during the transit between the collectors and the house. Pipes or (for air systems) ducts are, of course, heavily insulated whenever such outdoor routing is necessary. In addition, the pipes or ducts are buried underground. Still, some solar installers estimate a loss of ½ Btu of heat energy per hour for each foot of distance which the exchange medium must travel through unheated areas. For this reason 50 feet is usually considered the maximum practical distance between a remote collector array and an indoor storage tank.

Once the desired tilt angle is determined and a location is found that provides an acceptable southerly or near-southerly orientation, the question of shading must be considered. No matter how ideal the orientation and angle, all goes for naught if the collectors are shaded during that critical 9:00 A.M. to 3:00 P.M. period. Therefore, a close observation of the chosen collector installation spot should be made before any commitment is made to the system. Be especially watchful of the pattern of winter shadows, which are a good deal longer than those cast in summer (Fig. 4.8). Are there any trees in the area adjoining the collector site? If so, are they likely to grow tall enough to block the sun? If they aren't yours, can you offer to pay for pruning or removal? What about other buildings? Is the property next door owned by a neighbor, whose house will never get any bigger than it is now, or is it in the hands of a developer, who might decide to put up a high-rise? In ancient Rome

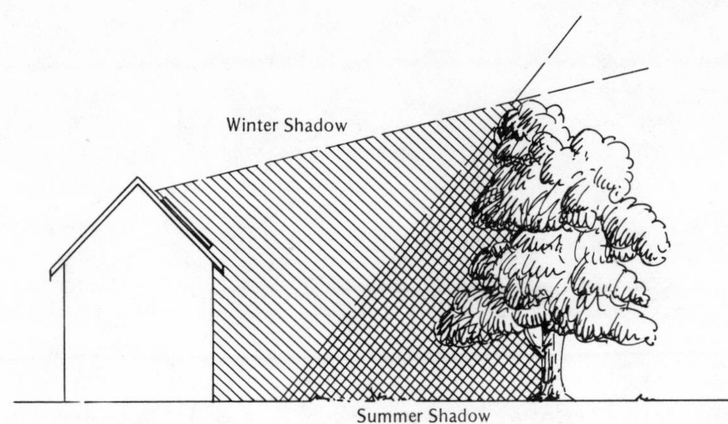

Fig. 4.8 Don't forget that objects throw longer shadows in winter. Although evergreen trees will be more of a problem than hardwoods, even bare branches can interfere with efficient solar collection.

it was illegal to build so as to block another's sunlight, but no such body of law has yet arisen here. There have already been several "sun rights" cases in the courts, and the question is surely one which will have to be addressed by the legislatures. In the meantime, though, we will have to rely on good sense in locating collectors and attentiveness to zoning and possible construction plans in the areas where we live.

Chapter 5

THE DOMESTIC HOT WATER SYSTEM

INSTALLING THE COLLECTORS

You and your installer have agreed on a location that offers proper orientation and freedom from shadows. Tilt angle has been decided. The installation crew is ready to get up on your roof and begin work. Or perhaps you are, in which case the manufacturer and seller of your system will have provided you with the necessary instructions. (If possible, do-it-yourselfers should buy from a retailer who also does installations. He will be more helpful if you need assistance or advice.) What follows here is *not* intended to be an installation manual, but an informal guide to the procedures used in mounting liquid flat-plate collectors for a typical home solar system. Much of the following also applies to the air-type collectors with some exceptions. With air, the manifold connections are different and the plumbing is necessarily replaced by ductwork. Ground installations are also similar for both kinds of flat-plate collectors except, of course, that the procedures used in securing the support frame to the rafters are eliminated.

The first two things that concern many homeowners when they first seriously consider a roof-mounted solar array are wind and structural stress. If a building is sound and the installer is competent, neither of these things should constitute a major worry. First, the weight of an array of solar collectors is spread over a considerable portion of the roof. One manufacturer's typical collector installation, for instance, weighs approximately 480 pounds, including the framework that provides the proper angle and secures it to the roof. It covers an area of 90 square feet. This results in a roof load of six pounds per square foot—hardly an excessive amount. If you are concerned about your roof, however, consult a housing engineer and ask your town building inspector if any local codes apply to weights placed on roofs. You should notify your inspector in any event, since local ordinances may apply to one or another aspect of the installation, and since a building permit may be required.

What about wind? A good solar installer will be able to tell you what wind speeds your collector array will be able to withstand. Test speeds of 140 and even 180 miles per hour are not uncommon. One installer when asked about the ability of four newly mounted collectors to withstand hurricane-force winds said, "Those panels are tested for a hundred and forty. If they go, the roof is going anyway."

The means of securing the collectors to the roof will vary depending on the model chosen and the shape of the support installation depends on the angle of the roof. Collectors mounted on a shallow-sloping roof will have to be bracketed higher at their upper ends in order to achieve the required tilt toward the sun. It is important to remember that even on roofs whose pitch is already sufficient, collectors cannot simply be mounted flush with the surface. They must be elevated slightly at both ends in order to allow rain to run freely beneath them. (See Fig. 5.1.)

Fig. 5.1 Although bracketing *(left)* is often necessary, some homeowners find that the pitch already followed by rooflines is acceptable for collector mounting *(right)*. (Courtesy Solar Solutions/Photos by Peter Southwick.)

The brackets themselves are frequently constructed of galvanized steel or aluminum pipe. Although collector mounting kits are supplied to installers by some solar manufacturers, it is common for installers to custom build brackets with pipe cut to the requisite length either in-shop or at the site. Modern connector devices make this a relatively simple task. If there is room for the possible addition of extra collectors in the future (for instance, if the homeowner decides to expand a domestic hot water system to take on space heating chores as well), the brackets may be installed so that an extension can easily be built on.

The finished bracketing will consist of members that form a frame running parallel and perpendicular to the roof line (Fig. 5.2), as well as vertical supports topped by a crossbar and extending as high as is necessary to hold the collectors at the proper tilt angle.

There are several options for fastening the brackets to the roof, all of which involve locating the rafters below. One simple method is to lag-bolt supportive struts into the rafters after drilling through the roofing and sheathing above (Fig. 5.3). Another is to loop a "U" or "J" bolt around the rafter with the threads protruding upward through the roof; support hardware can then be secured to the bolt and rafter with nuts

Fig. 5.2 Installers position galvanized-steel collector bracket on roof. This particular bracket was built on site, took less than two hours to complete.

Fig. 5.3 One method, using struts and clamps, of securing collector bracket to roof.

tightened from above. The way that the brackets can be fastened depends on what hardware, if any, the manufacturer has supplied and whether this hardware is already an integral part of the collector or will be attached on-site.

Once the struts or supports are secured to the roof and the bracket frame attached to them by means of pipe clamps (or whatever other hardware the situation requires), the collectors themselves can be brought up and installed. One of the more efficient means of completing the task is to fasten the collectors to the bracket frame with the same hardware that was used to secure the frame to the roof (Fig. 5.4). Once the job is finished, all points at which bolts enter the roof should be caulked over with a silicone sealant. The same sealant should be applied around the flashing through which the system's inlet and outlet pipes enter the roof.

Before going down the ladder and indoors to see how a hot water system functions, let's take a final look at the completed collector panel array. Here are two important features of a sound installation:

1. The collectors should be secured evenly, parallel to each other, with the entire array rising slightly toward one end so that there is no

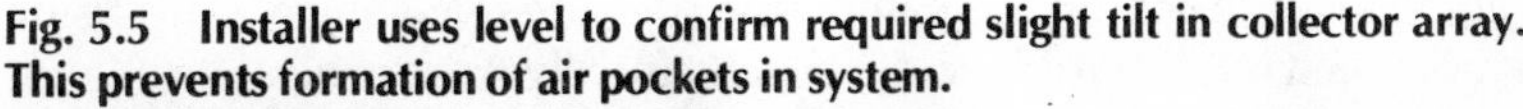

Fig. 5.4 In this installation, collectors are secured to bracket with same hardware that holds bracket to roof.

Fig. 5.5 Installer uses level to confirm required slight tilt in collector array. This prevents formation of air pockets in system.

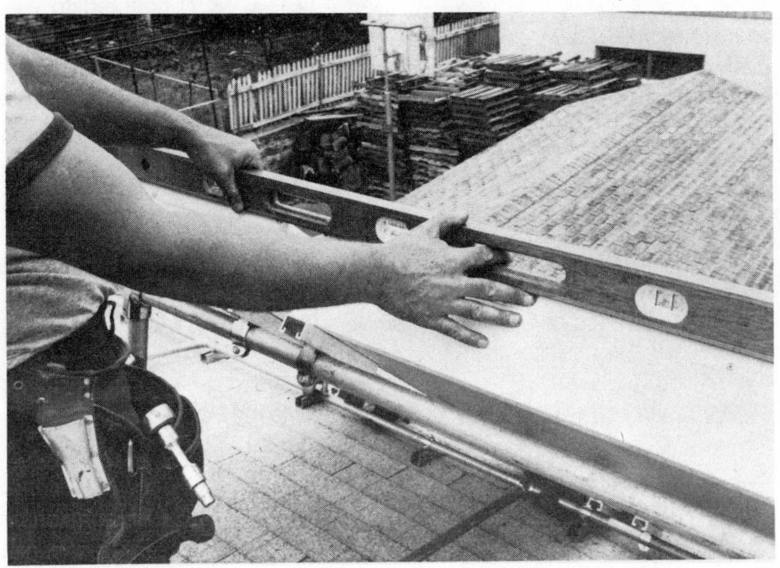

Fig. 5.6 Pressure relief valve on a domestic hot water collector array. Like all other exposed plumbing in system, valve will be covered with thick insulation.

blockage or "trap" in the path to the pressure relief valve. (This rising grade need not be visible to the eye but merely discernible with a level, as in Fig. 5.5.) The relief valve itself (Fig. 5.6) is connected to the manifold pipe at the top of the uppermost collector in the array. (On this collector the bottom manifold pipe is simply plugged.) The valve is set according to the manufacturer's specifications for the system and will release air but not fluid when there is a pressure buildup in the heat-exchange circuit.

2. Rigid insulation should be fastened around each of the manifold connections between the collectors. The space covered by these connections (that is, the distance between collectors) generally should not exceed three or four inches. The inlet and outlet pipes should also be securely insulated (Fig. 5.7) both above and below the roof surface.

HOW IT WORKS: HEAT EXCHANGE AND STORAGE

The collectors are on the roof (Fig. 5.8) and the storage tank is in the basement. In between lies some simple plumbing. (See Fig. 5.9.) How does it all work?

First, there are two basic types of liquid-circulating solar collection systems: the *drainback* (or *draindown*) and the *closed loop*. The difference between them lies in the ways they approach the problem of subfreezing nighttime weather.

While a solar system can collect heat efficiently during the daytime in winter, at night some provision must be made for preventing freezing of the liquid in the collectors and external plumbing. This can be done by draining all the liquid from the exposed parts of the system when a monitoring thermometer gives the warning; or by charging the system with an antifreeze solution instead of water.

Systems which incorporate the first type of low-temperature protection are called drainback (water drains back into a storage tank) or draindown (water drains down into an indoor holding sump). The drainback system requires a more powerful pump as it has to circulate a

Fig. 5.7 Rigid insulation partly installed around collector inlet pipe.

Fig. 5.8 Collector installation nears completion. Protective covering is removed from panels only after system has been charged with fluid.

greater volume of water. Both the drainback and draindown system must have a reliable series of valves and solenoids, and a thermostatic switch to make sure that all water drains down from the roof before the temperature falls low enough to endanger the plumbing and collectors. The advantage of these systems lies in the elimination of any need for separation of the heat-exchange medium from the water in the storage tank itself. Since all the liquid in the circuit is potable, the solar-heated water can flow directly into the tank and the exchange of heat is most efficient.

The closed-loop method of heat transfer derives its name from the fact that liquid heated in the collectors never comes in direct contact with the water in the tank; it instead makes a continuous circuit between the absorber plate tubing and an exchange coil located in the storage tank. This coil, heated by the fluid circulating within it, in turn heats the supply of water in the tank.

The increasing popularity of closed-loop installations in cold-climate domestic hot water and space heating systems is due partly to the smaller quantity of liquid which must be pumped (and thus the lighter pumps which can be used), and partly to their elimination of the

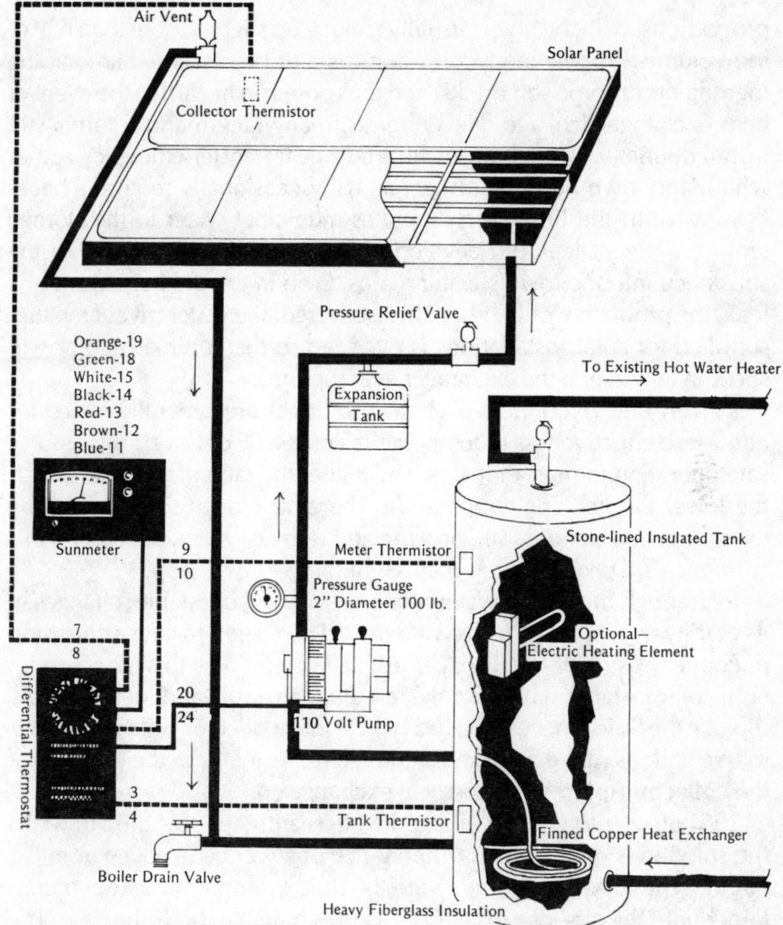

Fig. 5.9 Schematic of a typical solar domestic hot water system. (Courtesy American Solar Heat Corp.)

need for complicated mechanical fail-safe systems. Depending on the size and construction of the heat exchanger coil, the rate of flow of the antifreeze fluid, and the water temperature desired, a closed-loop system can be as little as five percent less efficient in heat transfer than the drainback or draindown variety.

The Heat-Exchange Medium

The antifreeze solution currently favored by many solar manufacturers and installers is a mixture of water and propylene glycol in near-equal proportions, with the glycol usually making up slightly more than half of the volume. Propylene glycol is non-toxic (it is even listed among the ingredients of some soft drinks) and thus poses no hazard in the event of heat exchanger leakage. Nevertheless, many tank manufacturers still install double-wall exchangers (this cuts heat transfer efficiency somewhat), and town building inspectors will occasionally require a backflow valve in the line which supplies municipal water to the storage tank. If a glycol leak did develop, this would prevent passage of the substance into the town's water mains. Even in the unlikely event of a leak, the problem would be easily discovered: the water-glycol mixture supplied for solar installations is dyed red so that a pinkish color will show in tapwater if the exchanger ever ruptures.

Propylene glycol heat-exchange solutions are generally mixed for antifreeze effectiveness to temperatures of −40°F or lower; this assures safe operation in most climates. The higher the ratio of glycol to water, the lower the freezing temperature. There have been some promising experiments with liquid silicon as an antifreeze element, but costs of this substance are prohibitive as of this writing.

Although the glycol-water mixture is reasonably stable, changes in its acidity over a three-to-five year period can begin to cause corrosion in copper. A simple litmus paper test can determine if this is occurring; your solar installer will make the test and can easily and inexpensively replace the fluid if necessary. In a typical four-collector system only four to five gallons of the mixture is required—this includes the contents of the collectors, plumbing, and heat exchange coil.

When a system is first charged with its antifreeze solution or when the solution is replaced, it is important that all air be expelled from the circuit. The installer will circulate the fluid to and from an open container until the absence of bubbles assures him that this is the case. The pressure of the liquid in the circuit will be kept within a preset range by a diaphragm type of expansion tank, similar to those in home hot-water heating systems, installed on the return line from the exchange coil to the collectors.

Circulating the Exchange Medium

A compact pump, mounted near or alongside the tank, circulates the fluid at a rate selected for optimum heat collection and exchange efficiency (Figs. 5.10 and 5.11). This rate figure will vary but it generally falls between one and five gallons per minute.

The pump does not operate continuously. For it to do so would be a waste of electricity since the water stored in the tank is not always cool

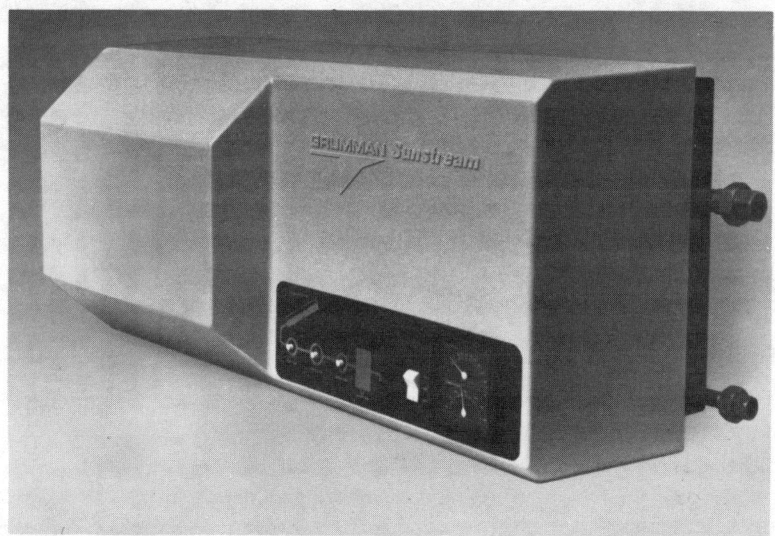

Fig. 5.10 Inside this new Grumman Sunstream module are almost all the components necessary to make a solar hot water system work in a freezing climate—heat exchanger, operating controls, and pumps. One end is connected to the water storage tank, the other to the solar collectors on the roof. The module reduces costs to the consumer by reducing installation time, and in some cases the need for a separate tank.

Fig. 5.11 A typical circulating pump for a solar domestic hot water system. (Courtesy Grundfos Pumps Corp.)

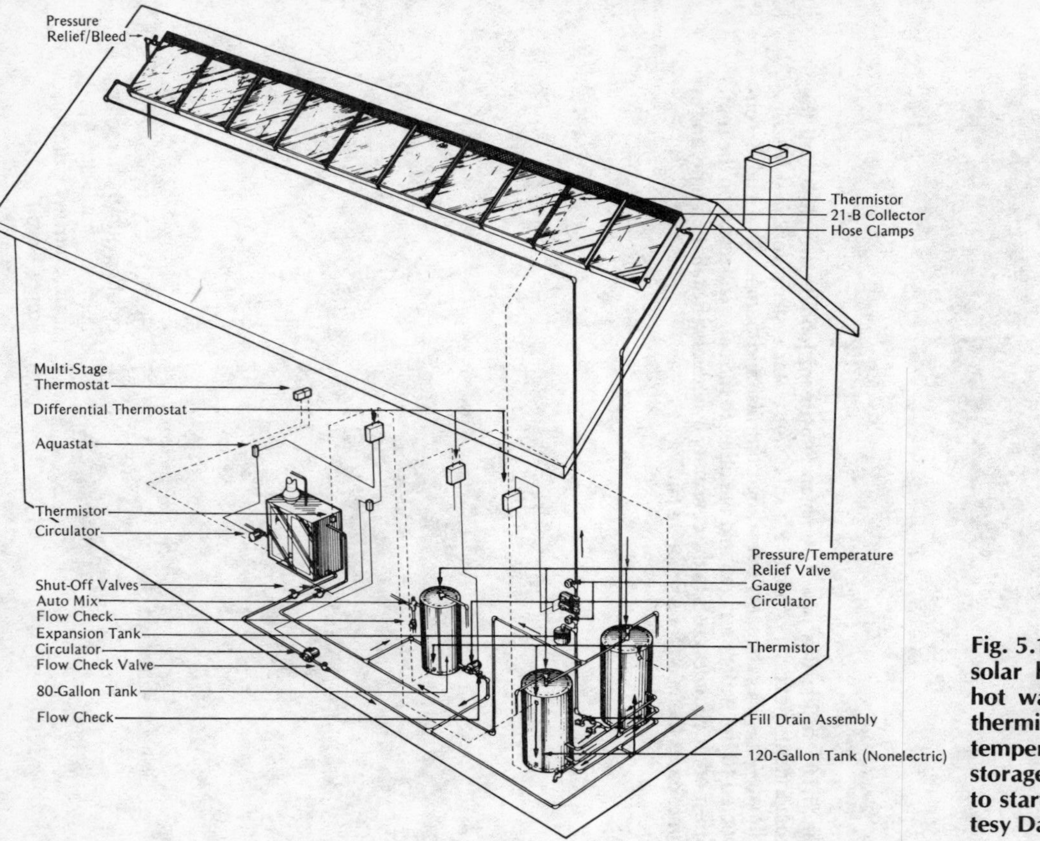

Fig. 5.12 Schematic diagram of a solar hydronic space and domestic hot water system. Note location of thermistors; these sense difference in temperature between collectors and storage, instructing circulator pumps to start and stop accordingly. (Courtesy Daystar Corp.)

enough to benefit from further circulation of fluid through the heat exchange coil. Here is how this circulation is regulated. Built into one of the collectors (usually one near the middle, if there are several in the array) is a heat-sensing device called a "thermistor." (See Fig. 5.12.) Another sensor is located in the storage tank. When the readings from these two points indicate that the temperature at the collector is sufficiently higher than that in the tank (a 20°F differential is usually the predetermined figure), the pump is automatically activated by a differential thermostat and heated fluid begins to flow down from the collectors, through the exchange coil, and back through the same cycle.

This not only prevents temperatures in the storage tank from falling too low, it also keeps intense heat from accumulating in the absorber plates of the collectors (the propylene glycol solution will boil at temperatures in excess of 250–275°F). A ¾ amp pump can generally accomplish this task in a total of six hours of operation per day. At five cents per kilowatt hour this equals $6.00 of electricity each year.

The desired effect in a system of this type is to have the fluid circulating in the heat exchange coil give up as much of its heat as possible before it leaves the coil (and the tank) and heads back up to the collectors. Coils are designed to assist in this process by presenting as large a surface as possible to the water in the tank. In one manufacturer's 120-gallon tank, the fluid circulating through an exchange coil that has 20 square feet of exposed surface will lose an average of 15° between the point at which the coil enters and that at which it leaves the tank (at a 3- to 5-gallon per minute flow rate). In another model with the same size tank and a larger coil the temperature exchange is even greater. Efficiency is also increased as the temperature of the incoming water supply drops: an exchange coil will give off more heat to colder water. This means a lot in the winter, when municipal mains sometimes deliver water at temperatures as low as 38°F. Even if the collectors cannot heat this water to the desired 120°F or 130°F level you can still save a lot of the energy that would have been required if a conventional heater were to do the whole job.

The Tank

This brings us to the tank itself. The purpose of a storage tank in a solar installation is not merely to hold water but to hold it at an acceptably high temperature for as long as possible. *Size* and *insulation* will help it do this.

It is a simple fact that a larger body of water will hold heat longer than a smaller one. Of course, it is also true that the larger quantity will take longer to heat up. When applied to solar heat collection and storage, this principle points up the necessity of properly matching the size of the tank. While a 60- or 80-gallon tank can be successfully served by a two or three collector array, at least three and ideally four panels are needed to efficiently warm the water in a 120-gallon tank. More precisely, since collector size varies, one square foot of collector area can adequately heat up to four gallons of water in storage. Once heated, though, this larger liquid mass will lose temperature more slowly. Although the size of the system you select will depend upon available space, expense, family size and hot water requirements, it is wise to keep this simple law of thermodynamics in mind.

Most tanks supplied with solar hot water packages are insulated even more thoroughly than those designed for storage of conventionally heated water. (See Fig. 5.13.) The innermost layer of a typical tank consists of an inch of spun artificial stone—"sort of a thermal concrete," as one installer describes it. Next are the first of two steel jackets and after that a two-and-a-half-inch layer of fiberglass such as that used in home insulation. Last is the outer steel jacket. After the tank is installed and the necessary plumbing connections are made, it is usually swathed securely in yet another blanket of insulation. A commercial-grade, faced fiberglass duct wrap in a one-and-a-half-inch thickness is a good

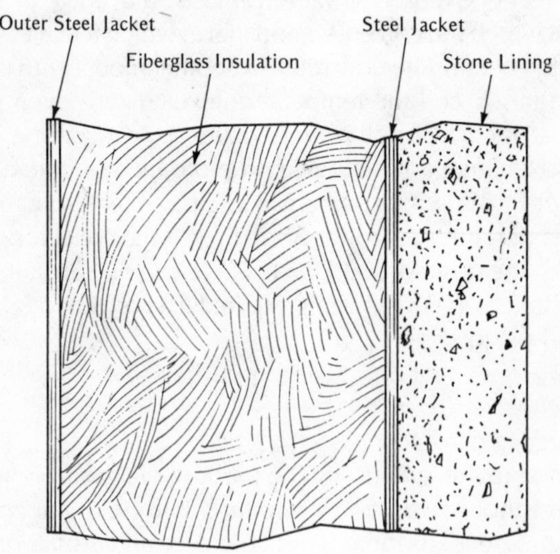

Fig. 5.13 Cutaway of typical solar hot water storage tank wall.

Fig. 5.14 Storage tank, pump, and controls for a solar domestic hot water system. Note insulation of pipes. Small cylinder mounted horizontally on wall is expansion tank. (Courtesy Lennox Industries.)

choice for this final covering. Pipes running to and from the collectors, to the auxiliary heaters, and to tap outlets are also insulated. Closed-cell flexible rubber insulation is satisfactory as is the rigid foam type with preformed elbows and bends. Use material of at least one-half inch thickness for indoor applications; one inch is recommended outdoors. (See Fig. 5.14.)

AUXILIARY HEATING FOR SOLAR DOMESTIC HOT WATER SYSTEMS

Throughout the summer (and occasionally even in colder weather) a properly sized and installed solar system can provide all or nearly all of a family's normal hot water needs. There are times, however, when auxiliary heating is required. This is not "the catch" to solar energy; even in cold regions the systems are routinely saving their owners 50 to 60 percent of their hot water heating bills. The practicality of solar energy is as real and as tangible as the dollar amounts those figures represent. The way that the rest of the hot water will be produced is up to the homeowner; whatever is needed will probably be provided by the conventional equipment in use before the solar installation.

Most solar hot water storage tanks now come equipped with a submersible electric heating element, which can be connected to a power source or not as the buyer desires. If connected, the element is thermostatically set to go on if the solar exchange coil cannot provide sufficient heat to bring the water up to the preferred tap temperature. Considering the price of electricity, however, it may not be economical to rely exclusively on this element as a back-up system especially if there is also a gas- or oil-fired tank-type water heater already in place. If so, the water from the solar tank—already preheated by the exchange coil—can be routed through insulated lines to the conventional heater, where the job is finished per the thermostat instructions. Some installers recommend sheathing the secondary heater tank with the same fiberglass duct insulation as the solar tank thereby preventing "stand-by" heat loss and increasing efficiency even further.

A similar routing of preheated water from the solar storage tank can be accomplished with a "tankless" system—the type in which tap water is heated by flowing through a coil in a furnace boiler. Since one of the biggest drawbacks of tankless domestic water heating is that it requires the furnace to go on throughout the summer, it is wise to install a solar system so that the furnace can be shut off and bypassed altogether at that time of year; the solar tank's own electric heating element can then be called upon to provide whatever extra heat is necessary. Chances are that this amount will be negligible.

INSTRUMENTS AVAILABLE

We saw earlier that the amount of heat transferred from the fluid in the exchanger coil to the water in the tank can be measured by means of thermometers showing the inlet and outlet temperatures of the exchanger fluid. In addition a typical system contains another thermometer to register the temperature of water leaving the tank for taps or for further heating, and a mixing valve (as on conventional heaters) to regulate this temperature if it is too high for home use. There is also a gauge that monitors the pressure in the closed fluid line and the performance of the expansion tank.

Further instrumentation is available for the homeowner with a more technical turn of mind or whose enthusiasm for a new solar system leads to a desire for a steady supply of information on its operation and efficiency. These instruments include the following:

1. A watt-hour meter to measure the amount of time during which the electric auxiliary element is in operation.
2. A similar device for keeping track of the amount of time the circulating pump operates. This not only provides a record of the cost of electricity to run the pump, but tallies the number of hours of solar collection as well.
3. A flow meter that records the amount of water that enters the storage tank from municipal lines. This gives a picture of family hot water use.

None of these last-mentioned gauges and dials are necessary, but they can add to the feeling of energy-saving resourcefulness which a home solar installation brings.

Chapter 6

SOLAR SPACE HEATING

The same principles of operation and basic collecting equipment used for solar domestic hot water heating can also be applied to space heating. The ways in which the details of storage and distribution can be worked out, however, are a great deal more varied than those used in simple hot water installations. There is no "state of the art" in solar space heating; the technology is constantly changing, and each manufacturer and system designer has his own idea about which combination of equipment and mode of operation is the most efficient. This is not to say that all systems installed several years back are obsolete and impractical, nor that any one way of doing things will emerge as *the* way in the future. There are too many kinds of homes, too many different climates, too many individual preferences for that to be so.

In addition to having some basic hardware in common, solar space heating and domestic hot water heating share some basic objectives, among them efficiency, simplicity of operation, and as short a payback time as is possible. The systems which survive the industry's early "shakeout" period will surely be those which offer these advantages despite their differences in design, construction, and operation.

Let us not underestimate the differences among solar space heating systems. There are many variables that may affect the choice of a solar space heating installation. Here follows a partial list of factors that may affect the selection of a system.

1. Architectural planning. If the house is still on the drawing board, it can be designed to make the best use of an active solar heating system. A lot of problems can be addressed during the planning stage of a new home. A clear southerly exposure can be arranged. Ample roof surfaces at the proper pitch can be provided. Landscaping to assure

Fig. 6.1 This home with a solar heating system is located in St. Mary's, Maryland. Three hundred square feet of Grumman Sunstream Model 200 solar collectors have been designed to supply 75% of the total space heating and hot water needs. This house contains 2,000 square feet of habitable floor area.

protection from winter winds is more feasible at this point. The home's indoor layout can be designed to accommodate sufficient radiator or convector surfaces, insulation, and storage for solar heat. In short, the structure will be much more of a passive solar house (built according to the principles outlined in Chapter 10 of this book), but will incorporate an active solar system into its design. Such homes are hybrids of the principles of active and passive solar systems and are the most efficient of all. (See Figs. 6.1 and 6.2.)

2. Retrofit capability. "Retrofit" is a word that sounds as if it were left over from the space program, but its meaning is simple. If you make any alterations to a building to make it more energy efficient, you are "retrofitting" the building. Such alterations could be minor, for example putting in weather stripping or storm windows, or major, as with the installation of an active solar system. Although almost any home will offer opportunities for energy-saving improvements, it is necessary first to take a close look at the structure to determine what can and cannot be done. Some houses—whether because of orientation, shading, or other

obstacles—are simply poor candidates for solar conversion. Work with what you have. If shade and direction are problems but firewood is cheap and plentiful, consider putting in a wood stove or furnace. In a rambling house that is too big or too poorly insulated for solar heat to contribute significantly to the home's energy expenditure, perhaps there is a suitable wing that could be separately zoned for a small solar system.

3. Climate. Winter temperature in your area may be too severe or cloudy periods too prolonged, for you to justify putting in solar equipment that supplies more than domestic hot water and a small percentage of the space heating requirement. Remember, the most efficient solar installations in very cold climates are those in houses designed for solar use, such as the Idaho residence described in the introduction to this book. It is possible in harsh climates to derive a major percentage of a conventional home's heating needs from an active solar system, but the

Fig. 6.2 Architect's rendering of a solar-heated home. Note minimum of window area at eastern exposure. (Courtesy Libbey-Owens-Ford.)

expense will be high and the payback period longer. Needless to say, though, this payback idea is relative: if heating oil prices continue to climb as they have over the past seven years, solar equipment will begin to seem like a cheap alternative anywhere south of the Arctic.

4. Expectations from a solar system. How much of your home's heat do you want your solar system to account for? Some people want a conversation piece; others want a workhorse that will take over from their conventional system in all but the most extreme circumstances, provided that their home design makes this feasible. After you have decided where your expectations fit on this scale, shopping for a solar system is not a simple matter of choosing a larger or smaller version of the same system. Some types of equipment work best in a major role; others are at their most efficient when installed in an auxiliary capacity. Decide what you want and learn what you can expect from the systems available. Despite the fact that there are unscrupulous and misleading operators in the solar energy business as in any other business, a large proportion of buyers' dissatisfaction comes from their own mistaken expectations of the equipment they buy. After selecting a reputable seller/installer, your next step should be to tell him what your requirements are and listen as he explains what his product can and cannot do in your home.

5. Existing heating plant. The type of heat generating and delivery system already in place in your home will have a lot to do with your selection of solar equipment. There are many ways of heating a home even if the objective is always the same. Most domestic heat in North America is provided by burning oil or gas or by operating electric furnaces. Direct radiant heat is also supplied by wood and coal stoves, by electric resistance panels, and by an assortment of gas or kerosene space heaters. There are also heat pumps; these are designed to remove heat from one source and distribute it to where it is needed.

In houses with central heating, steam, hot water, and forced hot air are the means of heat distribution. Steam and hot water heat both require plumbing lines that lead in turn to radiators or baseboard convectors. Hot air heat is carried through ducts and there are provisions made for a constant return of cool air from the rooms to the furnace for reheating. Obviously, there are many ways of tying a solar system into these different conventional heating plants, and many specialized types of solar collecting and distribution hardware designed to do the job.

Despite the fact that the conditions affecting the choice of solar system are so many and so diverse, there are certain features of collection, storage, and distribution that all solar heating systems have in common. First, the collectors must have the same orientation and angling (plus 15 degrees) as those which supply domestic water heat. Second, there is still a choice between closed-loop (antifreeze circulates through absorbers) and drainback/draindown systems (water draws down from collectors during winter nights). There are liquid storage systems designed for both of these modes of operation. The third principle relates to collector efficiency. Flat-plate solar collectors are more efficient when they operate at lower temperatures. That is, a collector can more efficiently heat large amounts of fluid (air, water, or antifreeze) to a moderately high temperature (90 to 120°F), than it can heat a smaller amount of circulant to 140 to 160°F or more.

There are also some general considerations about heat storage to be taken into account with any solar heating system. As we observed earlier, a large volume of water or any other mass gives up heat more slowly than a small amount. Also, the lower the temperature of the storage medium, the less rapidly it will lose heat. Taken together, these factors would seem to recommend an active solar heating system incorporating a relatively large, low-temperature heat storage facility. Many successful installations of this type are in operation; we will take a closer look at them shortly. But two features must be built into a house in order for it to derive a major portion of its heat from an unassisted system such as this: the large storage unit itself and the large areas of convector or radiator surface in the spaces to be heated. Not all homes can accommodate these features.

With these facts in mind, we can approach the question of whether an active solar heating system should operate independently from any conventional, auxiliary equipment that is in place, or whether it should instead operate in constant tandem with that equipment. If it is to operate independently, solar energy supplies all of the heat a house needs for as long as the supply in storage remains adequate. In larger installations, this can be as long as four or five days. After the stored heat is expended, an auxiliary furnace or space heater is called in.

If the solar and conventional equipment are to make up a team, storage capacity can be smaller, especially if the collectors are designed to operate efficiently at high temperatures. The purpose of the solar collectors in this case is to *preheat* a supply of liquid before it is routed to a conventional furnace or other heater. The advantages of this preheat function are clear. By definition a British thermal unit (Btu) is the amount of heat energy required to heat 1 pound of water 1°F. If the water temperature in a home heating system has already been raised substantially by energy from the sun, less of the expensive fossil fuel will be needed to bring the temperature up to the level required for the system's proper operation. Similarly, forced air warmed by solar-heated water can also be heated to the desired temperature with less expenditure of energy. (Systems in which air is both warmed in collectors and used as the heating medium will be discussed separately later in this chapter.)

A LARGE-SCALE SPACE HEATING SYSTEM

First let us consider a large hydronic space-heating system in which water heated by the sun is routed directly, after storage, into the home's baseboard convectors. This installation requires a large storage facility and a substantial collector area if it is to be relied on, unassisted, over a period of several days in a cold climate. As such, a large hydronic space-heating system is suitable for either a custom-designed house or one with existing features compatible with these requirements.

There are a number of options for the storage tank in this system. Tanks fall into two categories: site-built and prefabricated. There are advantages and disadvantages to both. Purchasing a ready-made storage tank generally enables the buyer to take advantage of the manufacturer's expertise regarding strength, leak resistance, insulation, and plumbing connections. However, there remain the problems of transportation and installation.

There is an old situation comedy routine about the man who built a boat in his basement and could not get it out. Conceivably a big solar storage tank could present the same dilemma in reverse. Some manufacturers are trying to reduce this risk by producing tanks which are delivered in separate sections and assembled at the desired location. Smaller tanks can also be used in a series. Of course, there is the alternative of outdoor underground storage as long as insulation requirements are met and the 50-foot maximum distance is observed.

If on-site tank construction is selected, fitting the unit into place is no problem, and the existing features of the building can be taken into account and perhaps even turned to advantage. However, it is the builder who assumes responsibility for leaks, insulation, and overall durability; there are no company warranties to cover these important areas.

Prefabricated tanks come in a number of shapes and materials; fiberglass and glass-lined steel have become standard in most applications. The steel tanks are generally cylindrical. They stand either vertically or horizontally and resemble larger sized versions of conventional hot water heaters. Fiberglass gives more design leeway; some tanks made of this material are even spherical.

Site-built tanks have generally been made of concrete. In fact, septic tanks are sometimes purchased and adapted to this purpose. A concrete retaining wall was built to bridge two existing walls in a poured concrete basement for one system that required a greater than usual storage capacity (its owner was out to get nearly all of his heat from the sun despite his New England location). The tank created by this partitioning provided a 16,000 gallon storage facility which, given the other particulars of the system and the requirements of the home, assured a five-day heat supply *without conventional assistance* even during the darkest winter days.

Concrete alone makes a poor storer of water and heat. Despite the material's strength its natural permeability will allow water to seep through, and its relatively low R value allows too much precious warmth to escape. These drawbacks can be eliminated by teaming the strong concrete walls with layers of insulation and waterproof plastic. The 16,000 gallon basement tank described above is lined with six inches of styrofoam; an equally thick layer of the rigid foam is used for a lid. The innermost surface, the one in actual contact with the solar-heated water, is a continuous 24-mil thickness of polyethylene.

Given the insulating properties of styrofoam panels, and the impermeability of heavy plastic sheeting, many do-it-your-self storage tank builders have found that concrete may be abandoned in favor of lighter materials, such as sturdy frames of wood or metal. There is room for invention as long as the basic qualities of sturdiness, heat-retention, and freedom from leakage are met.

The question of capacity should not detain us here for long since the size of the liquid storage tank to be installed in a home space heating system depends on factors that must be determined on a case-by-case basis. The first factor that affects capacity is the "heat load" of the house. The heat load simply refers to the amount of heat in Btus necessary each day to replace that which is lost by the structure. (For an explanation of heat load and how it is calculated for individual circumstances, see Appendix A.) The tank size, of course, also depends on the amount of heat that the solar installation will be asked to supply in relation to that provided by supplementary conventional equipment. In a cold climate, the best way to strike this compromise is to plan for enough solar heat contribution to justify equipment expense, but not so much that that expense will become excessively high. Also, do not plan solar heating needs according to the worst possible weather. That would drive your cost up and leave you with unneeded capacity during most of the winter.

In the hydronic heating system under discussion, the storage tank and the collectors are the only out of the ordinary components. The heat is delivered to the rooms of the house through conventional radiators or convectors. (*Convectors*, such as are now in use in most newer hot water and steam-heated homes, consist of finned pipes located in baseboards. The convectors first heat colder, floor-level air which then rises naturally and travels through vents or louvers, into rooms.) As we noted earlier it is necessary to increase the area occupied by radiators or convectors in each room in proportion to the decrease in the temperature of the water circulating through them.

In a conventional hot water heating system, the circulant is generally heated to between 90 and 160°F. If your solar equipment is only to be used as a preheating device, and if water temperature will regularly be boosted by conventional means to the level for which the distribution lines and radiators/convectors were designed, then no such increase in area is necessary. An all-solar installation in which the backup facilities only operate when stored solar heat is exhausted requires the necessary compensations.

In a direct storage-to-radiator system there will be at least two pumps: one to circulate water or antifreeze through the collectors, and one to send water, as needed, through the heating lines of the house. If antifreeze is used in the collectors, the system becomes a "closed loop"; a heat-exchange coil, similar to but larger than those used in solar domestic hot water tanks, will be used to effect the necessary transfer of heat. If the system employs a drainback or draindown mode of operation, however, the water heated in the collectors will flow directly into the storage tank. This mode, as noted before, requires no antifreeze. As with domestic hot water, the choice between closed-loop and drainback/draindown collectors involves weighing improved heat transfer against the need for providing mechanisms to prevent freezing.

While we are on the subject of heat exchange coils, we should note that there are two other capacities in which they can be used in this type of installation. It is possible to route the water for the heating lines themselves through an exchanger immersed in the tank. This makes the actual volume in the lines much smaller, and it enables the user to employ a smaller pump for this phase of the system's operation. If used with a closed-loop collector hookup, however, the loss in heat transfer efficiency will be compounded.

The other role a transfer coil can play in this situation is to heat domestic water supplies. Water from municipal lines would simply pass through a tank-immersed coil on its way to a conventional heater and to the faucets in the home. This modification is an extremely simple one if this type of space heating system is to be installed. It saves conventional fuel and helps the whole system pay for itself in a shorter period of time.

In a large storage tank for solar-heated water, temperature can vary as much as 15 to 25°F between the cooler bottom and the warmer upper portions of the stored fluid. This "stratification" of water in storage is due to the natural tendency of water, like air, to increase in buoyancy as it is heated. The warmer water rises; the cooler water settles. This is why the water being routed back to the collectors (in a drainback or drain-down system) is drawn from the lower reaches of the tank, and why water destined for radiators or convectors in rooms on the next floor is taken from nearer the top of the tank. If heat exchange coils are used, the same principle governs their relative locations.

In a conventional hydronic system hot water is pumped to where it is needed for space heating according to the instructions given by thermostats in the home's living areas. In a single-zone, one-thermostat system, water is circulated equally through all parts of the circuit. If there are two or more zones, a thermostat in any one part of the house can call for circulant water to only that area. Hot water is only circulated to the parts of the house that need the heat. The same provisions can be made in a water-circulating solar heating system (Fig. 6.3), but with the added feature of auxiliary equipment thermostatically set to go into operation when storage temperature falls below a specified point.

The circulation of water or antifreeze through the collectors is regulated according to the temperature differential between the storage facility and the absorber plates, just as in a simple domestic hot water system. When the water in the lower, cooler section of the storage tank has fallen 15°F below the temperature at the absorber (the differential may vary from one installation to another), the pump is activated and the heating of the storage water is resumed. In this way, the temperature difference never becomes so great that the collectors and pump must operate for a long time in order to restore usable heat. Nor does circulation stop and start incessantly: the pump shuts off when the temperature gap has been narrowed to 3°F or so.

In some experimental drainback systems the collectors supply heated water directly to an auxiliary heat source and the radiator/convector lines during times when the sun is bright but the storage heat is exhausted. This would seem impractical in most circumstances since

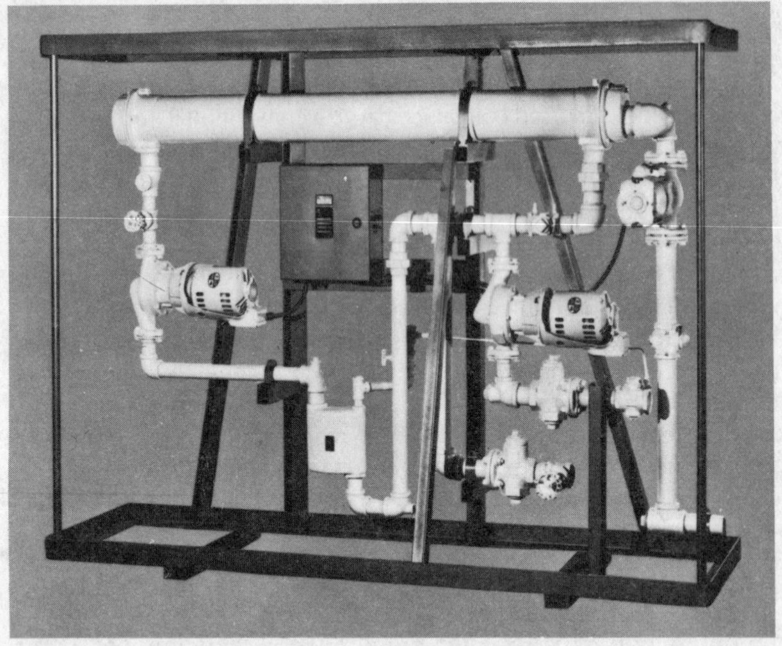

Fig. 6.3 Controls and dual circulating pumps for a typical solar hydronic space heating system. (Courtesy Bell and Gossett/ITT.)

the pump which circulates water through the collectors is often designed for a smaller load than that which circulation through the entire hydronic system would require, and since the ideal flow rate for solar collection and that recommended for heat exchange in the rooms may not be equal.

Backup Heating

A solar heating system such as the one described above ordinarily would be installed as primary, not auxiliary, equipment. Nevertheless, conventional backup would be required. We noted earlier that the installer would have the option of linking the two systems so that the collectors and the storage tank serve to preheat, or isolating the solar from the conventional heat sources, so that an "either-or" function is assumed.

In most full-sized, hydronically heated homes whose owners have opted for a solar system with a large storage capacity, the solar-heated water is channeled through either a gas- or oil-fired boiler or an auxiliary tank with an electric heating element. None of this equipment will be required to function, however, unless several days' bad weather have forced storage temperatures down past the point where they can supply enough heat to the rooms. When the conventional, backup heaters do go into operation, it will only be to finish the water-heating job. In a house with a fuel furnace already in place, the solar installer's main task will be to assure that the furnace's thermostatic controls allow the backup to step in only when it is actually needed. In a new home, or in one in which a new furnace is to be installed, the conventional unit will have to be sized so as to meet the heat load of the entire home. Even though it will only be operating for part of the time, there will be times when it has to heat all of the house.

Completely separate backup systems are quite another matter. Roughly speaking, they could be divided into those which are thermostatically controlled and thus automatic, and those which must be activated by hand when needed.

Since it would be impractical to consider installing an entirely separate hydronic heating system that uses water other than that drawn from solar storage, the independent backup most commonly chosen for a full-sized home is radiant electric (resistance) heat. (The term "resistance" refers to the heat-producing passage of electric current through the electrically resistant materials of which the panels' heating coils are made.) This is not to be confused with an electric furnace in which electric elements heat forced air currents prior to their distribution to room registers. Electric resistance heat is provided by the easy to install but expensive to operate radiant baseboard panels.

Except for occasionally heating individual rooms, this type of heat is no longer as popular as it was when electric rates were low and the "all-electric home" promised to be the wave of the future. Its justification as a back-up system in a solar house depends upon the capacity of the solar installation and the climate in which the building is located. It is an admirable goal—and often a quite feasible one—to derive 50 percent of a home's heating energy from the sun in a cold climate.

To count on electricity for the rest defeats a homeowner's money-saving intentions as well as any ecological motivations which he or she may have. Electricity, it is sometimes argued, is 100 percent efficient, that is, it yields all of its energy potential as heat. That is true at the point of use, but this energy-efficiency level does *not* hold up in the process of manufacturing electricity. At the other end of the power line, energy is being lost at the rate of approximately three Btus for every one produced. Transmission lines account for further loss.

Radiant electric heat, then, is a wise choice for solar backup only if the sun can be reasonably counted on to provide a clear, steady majority of a home's heating needs, or if the climate is mild and only an occasional supplement is needed. Electricity *can* still be a useful auxiliary in water-heating systems in which the fluid has already been substantially preheated by the sun. The low cost of electric heating elements for hot water systems makes the use of electricity particularly attractive.

If radiant electric heat is representative of the automatic, thermostatically controlled options, then the wood stove is most characteristic of the manually operated backup alternatives. Obviously, a wood stove is not going to go on by itself while you are away; nor is a single stove going to heat an entire full-sized house when the heat supply in a solar storage tank is exhausted.

Wood can be just as valuable a source of auxiliary heat in a home partially dependent on solar energy as in a conventionally heated structure. By keeping room temperatures sufficiently high, a stove can prevent thermostats from ordering hydronic circulation; this results in less transfer of heat from the water in storage, and also in less frequent operation of whatever electric or fossil-fueled alternatives are involved.

In a small house, of course, an efficient, properly sized wood stove can even pick up the entire load when there is no solar heat in storage. As long as someone is home to tend the stove, the solar and wood units can pair up to keep the furnace off during a great majority of the time. Portable electric space heaters can also play a part; although for the reasons outlined earlier, it is foolish to rely upon them extensively over a long period of time or in areas of intense cold.

ALTERNATIVES TO HYDRONIC HEATING

Many homes already have the plumbing and radiators or convectors used in hydronic heating, and, as we saw above, certain types of solar installations are perfectly compatible with them. But other homes have always been heated by forced warm air; instead of pipes and convectors, they have ducts and registers. Not only can a liquid-circulating solar collector array and storage tank serve these homes; some professional installers have even gone so far as to recommend installation of ductwork where none already exists in order to take advantage of what they feel is a simpler, more efficient solar heat distribution system. The secret, once again, is the heat exchange coil. Only this time the coil is outside the storage water tank and it heats air rather than another liquid.

In a forced-air heating system, a central blower directs the flow of air through the rooms. Return registers, located near the floor, draw in cool, heavier air that is then pulled by the blower into the heat exchange chamber of the furnace. From there the heated air passes into outlet ducts, from which it is distributed back to the rooms. The furnace goes on as often as is necessary to keep the cycling air warm enough to satisfy the thermostat setting.

How does solar hot water assist in this process? It is simply a matter of intercepting the returning air before it reaches the furnace. The furnace has been instructed, by the thermostat, to heat the circulating room air to a certain temperature. If the air that reaches the furnace's heat exchanger has already attained this temperature, there is no need for the furnace to go on; if it is partially heated, the furnace has only a supplementary task to perform.

The heat-exchange coil, then, extends from the solar hot water storage tank and is contained inside the return air duct. The copper tubing of the exchanger coil, which is usually finned for greater contact with the air, gives up heat to the passing draft. This heat is replenished by storage tank water circulated through the coil at a set rate, and the cycle continues. The air reaching the furnace is warm enough so that significant fuel savings result. (See Fig. 6.4).

Because of the temperature stratification principle described earlier, the heat exchange coil outlet will be at a point near the top of the storage tank, while the inlet (return from the duct) will be lower. But the tank itself generally need not be as large as that used in an hydronic installation; water for some modest systems can even be drawn from a large-sized domestic hot water tank (approximately 120 gallons) or from a pair of such tanks. The lines between the tank(s) and the return duct should be insulated as carefully as any other exposed solar water pipes especially if they must travel through an unheated space.

Given the size of your house and the volume of air which is handled by your furnace/blower combination, a competent installer will be able to calculate the required number of collectors, size of storage facility, and rate of flow for a system that will provide both duct air preheating and domestic hot water.

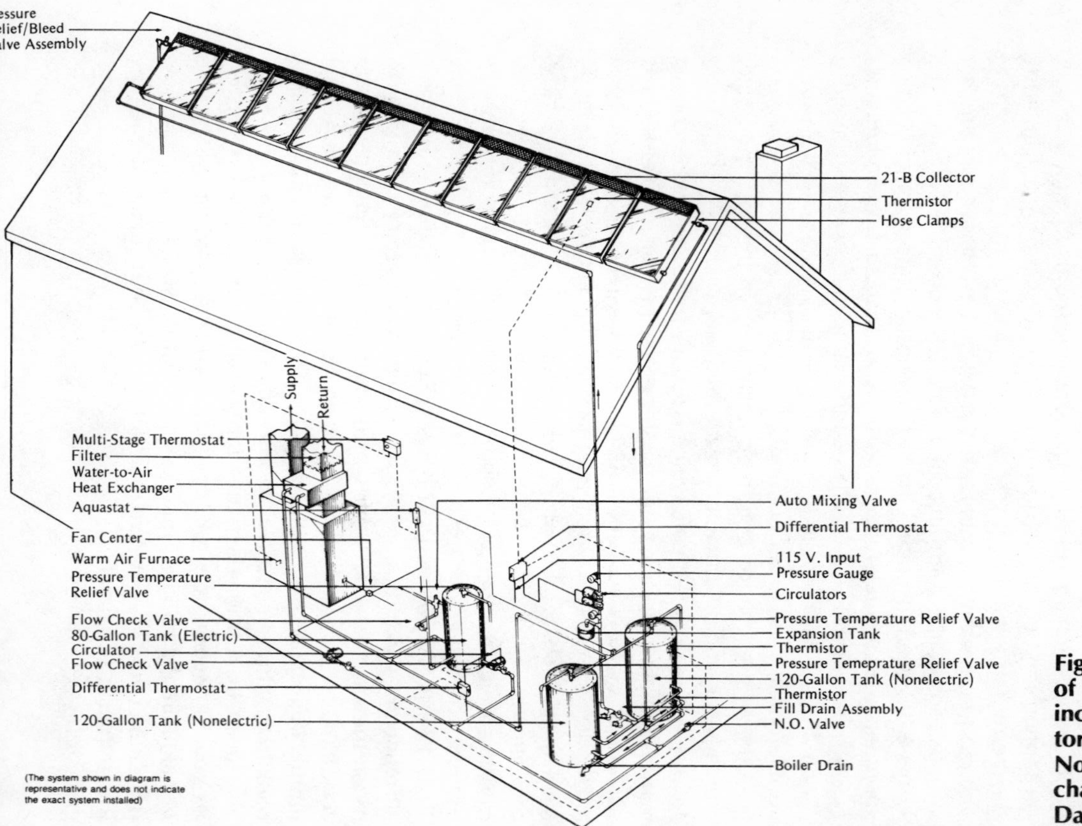

Fig. 6.4 Schematic diagram of a space heating system incorporating liquid collectors and air distribution. Note water-to-air heat exchanger at left. (Courtesy Daystar Corp.)

SOLAR ASSIST FOR HEAT PUMPS

One of the more promising developments in space heating has been the teaming of solar hardware with heat pumps. Many experts feel that solar-assisted heat pump installations represent a means of bringing out the best in both technologies. What is more, there are a variety of ways in which the combination can be made.

Although the heat pump has been around for years, and although it operates on much the same principle as does an air conditioner, it remains a mystery to many homeowners. Before examining the heat pump's role in solar heating, let us review the process by which it extracts and distributes heat.

The heat pump does not create heat as does an electric or fuel-fired furnace. Instead it *moves* heat from one location to another. That procedure is all very simple when the heat *source* (the place from which the heat is being moved) is warmer than the heat *sink* (the place to which the heat is being transferred). Heat naturally flows from a warmer to a cooler object or environment. But a heat pump must reverse this process, since its job is to take heat from the cold outdoors and use it to warm indoor areas.

This may sound impossible, but it is based on simple facts. There is always some heat available outdoors even on the coldest days; if there were none, the temperature would be absolute zero, or approximately −460°F. It does not even get that cold in Minneapolis. As long as it stays above 40°F or so, most heat pumps are able to extract sufficient heat from the outside air (or, as we will see later, from a stored supply of water) to raise temperatures indoors. When it is colder out, the machine's efficiency decreases. This is when solar energy can provide useful assistance. (See Fig. 6.5.)

A heat pump extracts heat from "cold" environments by circulating a refrigerant gas through the condenser and the evaporator coils in much the same way as a refrigerator or an air conditioner. In an air conditioner the refrigerant gas is compressed as it is pumped from the indoor to the outdoor coil, and it is allowed to expand as it is cycled back to the inside coil. The gas cools as it expands thereby absorbing heat from its surroundings. It "dumps" this heat outdoors, and the indoor cooling process continues. In a heat pump the refrigerant is instead allowed to expand as it travels into the outdoor coil. Because of the nature of this gas, expansion causes it to cool to a temperature even lower than that of the air surrounding it. It draws heat from this air and gives it up upon entering the house and being squeezed by the com-

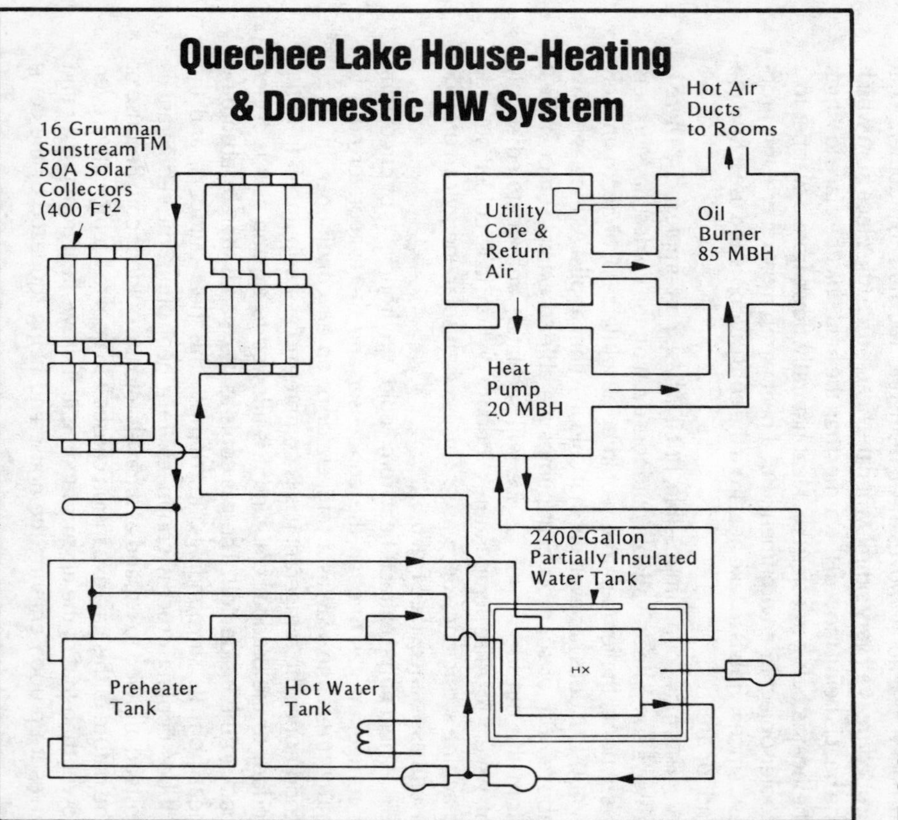

Fig. 6.5a In this installation, low temperature collectors made possible the use of the heat pump under extreme cold conditions. Solar energy increases the coefficient of performance of the heat pump which is on all the time.

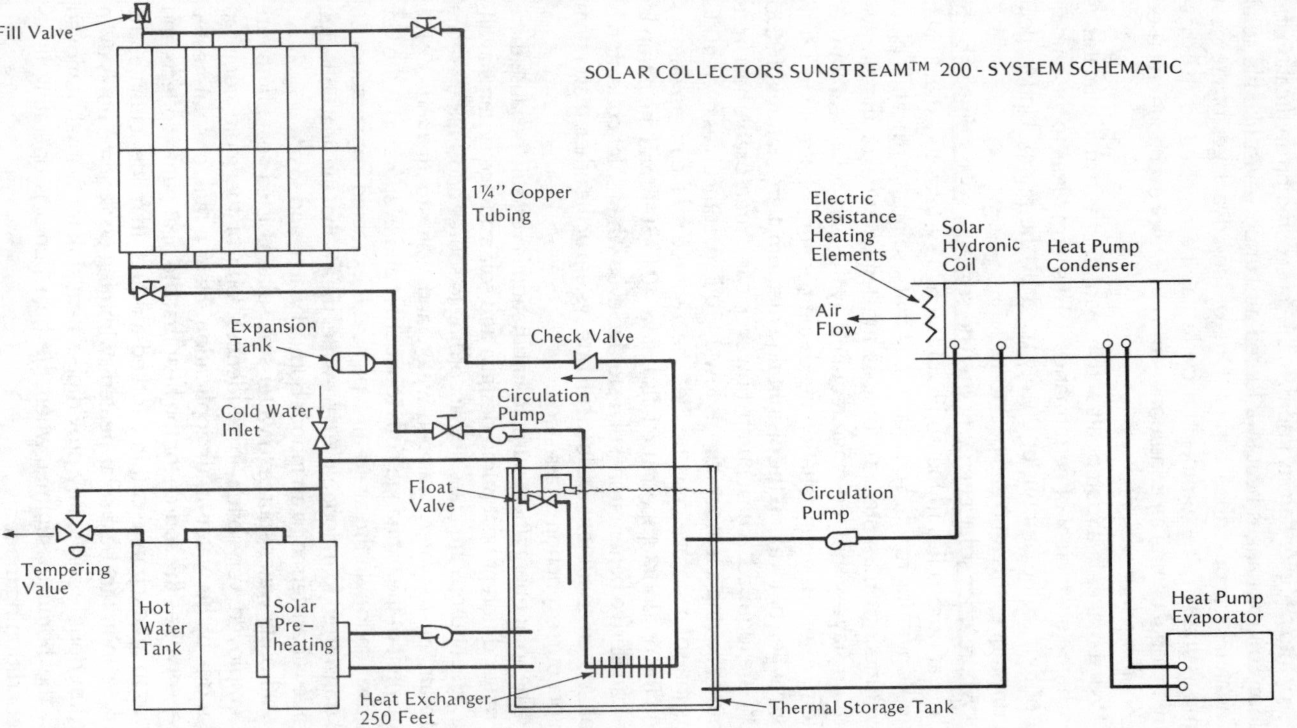

Fig. 6.5b In this space heating system, the heat pump is the back-up when insufficient solar heat is available.

pressor into a higher density liquid. In the most common application the indoor coil exchanges heat to a forced-air current—just like the solar hot water loop described earlier. One of the advantages of the heat pump is that in the summer the cycle can be reversed to that of a conventional central air conditioner, and the indoor exchange coil used to cool forced-air currents.

What makes heat pumps attractive, particularly in mild climates, is their high "coefficient of performance." This term refers to the ratio of Btu output to the amount of energy used by the pump. Under ideal circumstances this ratio can be 3 to 1.

Where does solar energy fit in? The secret of solar compatability with heat pumps lies in the ability of the two systems to extend each other's operating range. You may recall that a solar space heating plant may function unassisted as long as the temperature of the storage medium stays within the range required by the particular heat transfer system. A forced-air installation needs temperatures in the 80 to 130°F range; when hot water is the distribution medium, temperatures of 90 to 160°F are required. A heat pump, however, can extract usable heat from a source having a temperature as low as 50°F, or sometimes even 40°F. Thus the solar storage can provide a heat source for the pump on days when the outdoor temperature falls below 40 to 50°F, and the pump in turn can derive benefit from solar storage even when solar collection is weak. When conditions are ideal for one system or the other, that system can of course function unassisted.

The solar energy/heat pump combination is versatile because there are many different heat pump designs and solar storage systems available. Heat pumps are classified according to source and sink; there are air-to-air, air-to-water, water-to-water, and water-to-air models. The placement of the exchange coils (condenser and evaporator) is the key to classification. In the air-to-air type heat is extracted from outdoor air and transferred to indoor air. Air-to-water means that the heat collected outside is transferred to an indoor body of water, and so on.

Although water-source to water-sink solar-assisted heat pumps are not employed very often in residences, one of the more common variations is the water-to-air application. Here a tank of solar-heated water serves as the source for the heat that the heat pump collects and moves to an exchange coil in a forced-air duct. In milder climates the "tank" can in fact be a solar-heated swimming pool. Some pools even perform double service by providing a heat sink for warmth removed from the home in summer when the heat pump is operating in its air-conditioning mode.

In an entirely different vein, the functions of the solar and heat pump systems can be kept separate yet compatible if a solar-heated exchange coil is routed to an air-to-air pump's forced-air return duct. With this approach, the task of the heat pump can be reduced by the solar preheat function, just as a conventional furnace's load is lightened when the same provision is made.

There are also systems in which an air-to-air heat pump uses as its source the warmth collected by air-type collectors and stored in rock bins. These installations, as well as those mentioned above, are best if designed so that solar energy can do the entire heating job whenever possible. Still, the heat pump may be a valuable asset with which to extend the useful temperature range of solar storage.

Heat pumps are by no means new to the market, and those produced within the past few years are a good deal more sophisticated and reliable than those which first gained attention in the 1950s. Careful shopping—both for a manufacturer and an installer—is still in order. Do not let anyone sell you a heat pump/solar combination unless he understands both and can make a realistic appraisal of the system's practicality in your area. In colder climates, frequent dependence on backup equipment (especially electric heat) may make the investment in a heat pump and solar hardware unjustifiable. Finally, do not forget that heat pumps are always more economical when the climate makes it practical to use them in reverse cycle for air conditioning.

AIR-TYPE FLAT-PLATE SOLAR COLLECTORS

We have seen how liquid flat-plate collectors can provide heat energy for both hydronic and forced-air home heating systems. A solar installation can be built to run entirely by means of air circulation if air-type flat-plate collectors are used. These collectors are nearly identical to liquid collectors in outward appearance. However it is air, not water or antifreeze, that is circulated past the absorber plates in order to collect heat. (See Fig. 6.6.)

The question of whether air or water is a superior solar heat exchange medium has been around as long as the collector industry itself, and it seems that there are enough pros and cons to prevent either from eclipsing the other. One large manufacturer of liquid collectors is working to produce its first air system. One leading manufacturer of

Fig. 6.6 The rooftop panels in this photo are air-type collectors, designed to supply a significant portion of the home's space heating. (Courtesy Solaron Corp.)

air-exchange units has recently acquired a smaller company that makes liquid flat-plate collectors.

There are a number of things to be said for air systems. First, the equipment is lighter and frequently easier to assemble on-site or build from scratch. Second, there is no danger of freezing, which means that drainback or antifreeze-heat exchange provisions need not be made. Third, leaks are not a problem. This is not to say that a gap or hole in the ductwork will not cut system efficiency, but air is not destructive to the areas surrounding a leak. Fourth, installation is easier, provided that room for ducts exists, since no soldering or brazing of copper pipes is required. Finally, the lower transfer temperature used in forced-air home heating enables the collectors to operate more efficiently and with less heat loss from their surfaces.

There are drawbacks to air-type installations. The ductwork necessary for heat distribution takes up more space between floors and within walls than does the plumbing which supplies a hydronic system. If this space is not available, there is little that can be done to remedy the situation, although closet space can sometimes be pressed into service. It should be noted, however, that most American homes, and certainly a clear majority of the newer single-family structures, employ forced-air heat and thus already have the necessary ductwork.

The storage facilities used in air-type solar installations can also cause space problems. Rock is the usual storage medium in these sytems, and it simply cannot store as much heat as an equivalent volume of liquid. In fact, it is estimated that a body of water can hold 2½ times as much heat as a supply of rock contained within the same dimensions. However, some promising work has been done with space-saving alternatives to rock. We will examine these substances later on in this section.

The remaining objections to forced-air heat, solar or otherwise, are relatively minor. Some people object that the blowers used to move air are noisier than liquid-circulating pumps; but the newer equipment runs smoothly and silently, and is already in widespread use. There are also complaints of dryness in air-heated homes. A built-in humidifier is the answer, and it can be installed as easily in a solar forced-air system as in a conventional one.

How does the inside of an air-type solar collector differ from the liquid models? For one thing, air circulated through a collector does not have to be routed, as a liquid would, through specific channels bonded to the absorber plate. Air comes in contact with every part of the absorber. Manufacturers and do-it-yourselfers have come up with a variety of ways to direct air past the absorber. (See Fig. 6.7.) In some models the current flows over the plate; in others it flows beneath; and in still other designs, an above-and-below combination is found. The below-plate air circulation seems to work more efficiently as the collector temperature increases. Regardless of the path taken by the forced air, any surface within the collector that makes contact with the flow should be painted black.

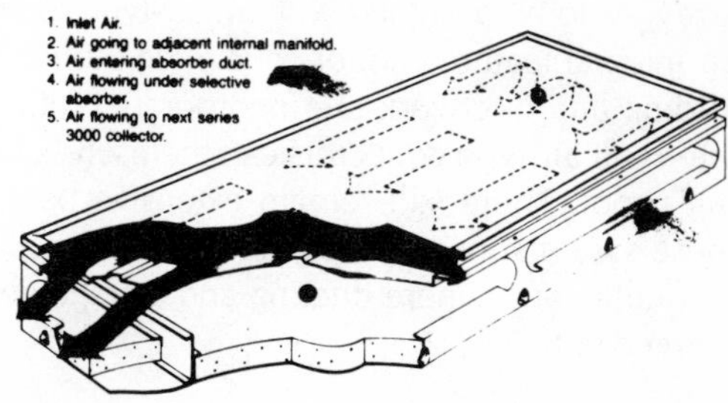

Fig. 6.7 Diagram shows flow patterns in an air-type collector. (Courtesy Solaron Corp.)

One of the peculiarities of air flow is that as an undisturbed current of air flows across a hot surface, only the lower portion of it receives the maximum amount of heat. The smoothly flowing current of air develops strata that move at different speeds; those closer to the surface travel slowly and become hotter, while the faster flowing air fails to pick up heat. For this reason the absorber plate in an air-type solar collector is usually designed to create turbulence in the air currents that are forced above or below it. Any number of baffles and plate configurations have been tried—fins, corrugations, perforations. One do-it-yourself plan even suggests a series of black-painted beer cans halved lengthwise to cup the passing air and toss it about. It is doubtful whether any consensus will be reached on the ideal pattern. Experts warn that excessive air turbulence can cause a pressure drop, which will in turn make a more powerful blower necessary in order to maintain correct flow rates to living areas and storage. A package installation can often be superior, one reason being that the manufacturer can coordinate collectors, blowers, and prescribed rate of air flow.

The rest of the air-type collector—housing, insulation, and glazing—is very similar in appearance and construction to the basic liquid models. However there have been attempts to radically depart from the basic design. One of the most successful of these innovations is an adaptation of the SolaRoll™ collector described earlier in this book. For air circulation, the product's manufacturers simply suggest installing the flexible framing strip, along with glazing, above a blackened and insulated surface. The absorber mat, with its built-in tubing, is not used.

The *manifolds* in an air-type system are the conduits that carry air from one collector to another, and to the supply and return ductwork that serves the storage and living areas. Manifolding can be external, or it can be built into the collectors as in the Solaron™ system. The latter design enables an array of collectors to be assembled with only one inlet and one outlet duct (Fig. 6.8). Also, the absence of external manifolding leaves more space in the attic area immediately below the collector array. A home designed with an air-type solar space heating system as an integral feature can, of course, be built so that the necessary manifolding and ductwork are incorporated into the structure of the roof. Site-built air-type collectors can themselves form a part of a new building's roof. There still remain extensive possibilities for incorporating these systems into existing homes where climate and orientation are favorable, and where ducting and storage details can be satisfactorily worked out.

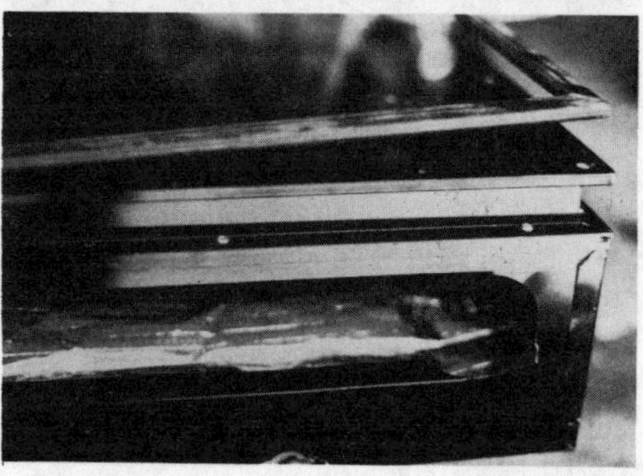

Fig. 6.8 Photo above shows manifold connections on Solaron air-type collector. Below, partial dissassembly of same unit shows glazing and insulation. (Courtesy Solaron Corp.)

STORAGE SYSTEMS FOR AIR-TYPE SOLAR HEATING

The most formidable design problem to be dealt with in the air-exchange system is storage. We noted earlier that if a bin of rocks and a tank of water were confined to the same dimensions, the water would hold more than twice as much heat as the rocks. Obviously, then, an air-type system using rocks as a storage medium will require a greater amount of storage space. This volume need not necessarily be contained within a box with sides of equal or near-equal dimensions; rock storage bins have been built to conform to available room in basements, crawl-spaces, and even unusual or "dead" spaces within building walls. One solar pioneer, Dr. George Löf, has had success with storage units consisting of vertical fiberboard cylinders inside his home. An advantage to placing the heat storage facility within the heated areas

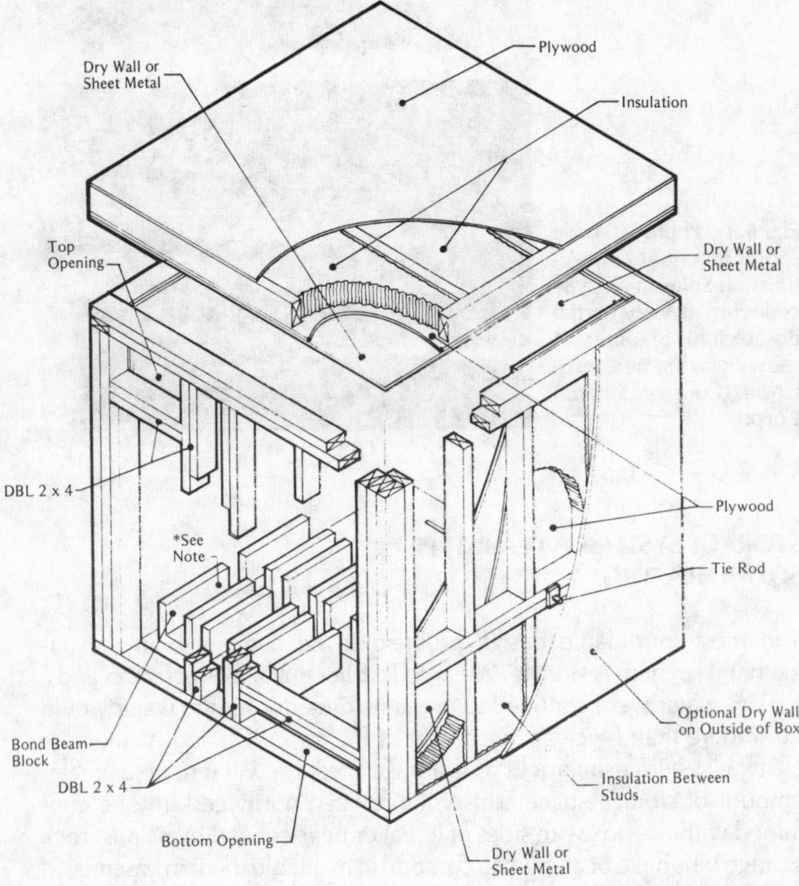

Fig. 6.9 At left, one possibility for rock storage in an air-type system. Drawing

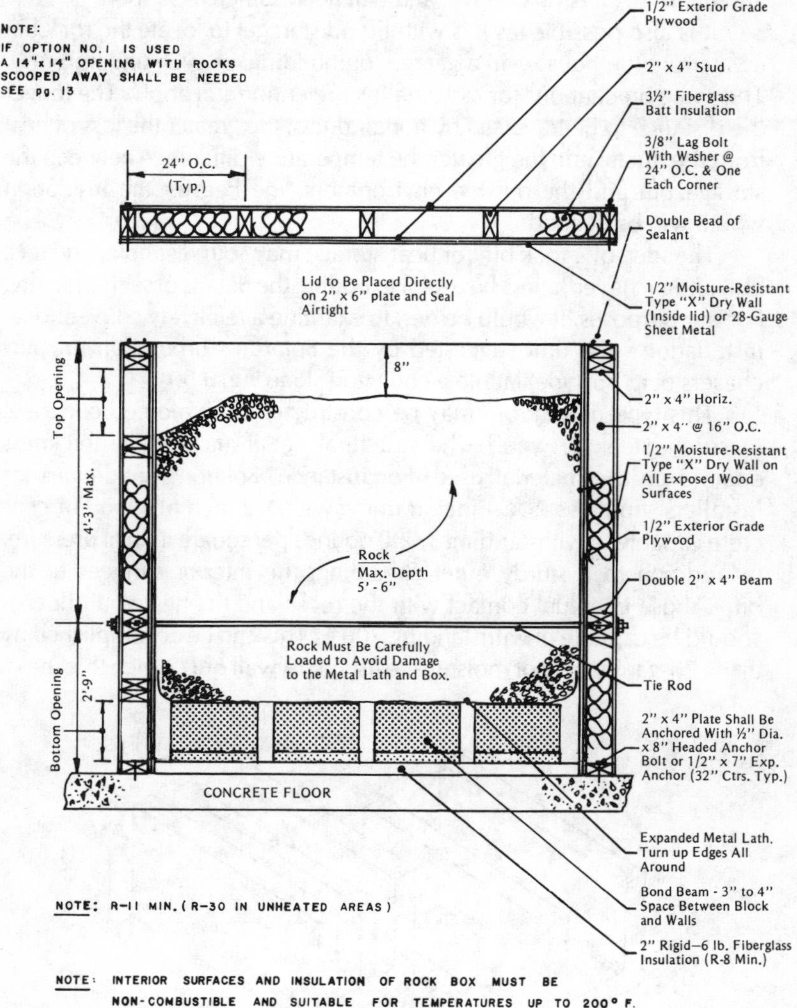

at right shows placement of rock in bin. (Courtesy Solaron Corp.)

of a building is that heat lost from storage helps warm these areas rather than dissipating to the outdoors or to an unheated basement. Otherwise, secure insulation of the rock bin is required, just as it is for liquid facilities. One word of caution: don't locate any heavy heat-storage fixture, whether it contains rocks or water, on unsupported floor areas above basement level. Think of the storage bin as you would a hearth and chimney: it is very heavy, and will need sufficient support.

It is also possible (as it is with liquid storage) to locate the rock bin away from the house—in a garage, outbuilding, or even underground. The same precautions for assuring heat retention still apply. The longer the distance to be traversed by hot air ducts, the greater the loss of heat from the ducts; and the greater the temperature difference between the storage bin and the outside environment, the heavier the insulation which will be needed.

The idea of a rock bin for heat storage may sound simple, and it is, but it might nevertheless be useful to outline the details of such a facility. For our purposes, it would be best to examine a relatively conventional installation—the unit suggested by the Solaron Corporation for purchasers of its air-type flat plate collectors. (See Fig. 6.9.)

This type of rock bin may be constructed of reinforced concrete, masonry, steel, or wood. The structural detail and surface thickness depend on the material used. For instance, Solaron's guidelines for installers stipulates 2 × 4 inch framing with 1/2 inch plywood or concrete capable of withstanding 3,000 pounds per square inch of pressure. In addition to a sturdy outer sheathing, the interior surfaces of the bin—those in actual contact with the rocks and the heated air flow—should be capable of withstanding 200°F. This can be accomplished by using 28-gauge steel or moisture-resistant drywall of 1/2-inch thickness.

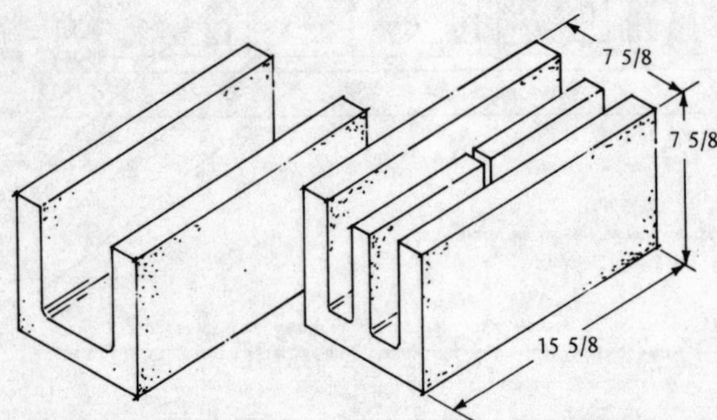

Fig. 6.10 Use bond beam blocks to support metal lath and rocks in storage bin. (Courtesy Solaron Corp.)

The rock bin is generally insulated with rigid fiberglass boards and/or fiberglass batting, with the rigid boards being the material of choice for the bottom of the bin, and batting for the plywood lid. Walls, depending on construction, can accommodate either. A minimal R value of 8 is recommended.

The rocks in the bin are not simply piled from the bottom to the top. A typical design allows for a "plenum," or open-air space, at both ends of the fixture. Solaron suggests that this be accomplished by placing bond beam blocks at the bottom of the bin and covering them with a layer of diamond-mesh galvanized metal lath. (Bond beam blocks are similar to standard concrete blocks but open at the top, so that from the end they look like the letter "C" or an "E" lying on its side—see Fig. 6.10.) The lath mesh, of course, will not allow the rocks to fall through to the bottom. It is through this void space at the bottom of the bin that cool air is routed to and from the rooms of the house.

The rocks themselves must conform to certain specifications. The number of rocks depends on the size of the bin (this in turn, of course, depends on the storage capacity desired) and the rate at which solar-heated air is blown past the rocks. In any system of any size the rocks must be clean. They are generally washed at the site where they are obtained or immediately prior to being stored in the bin, but the rocks are *never* washed after they are in place. The smooth, round stones that commonly line the banks and beds of streams ("river rock") are ideal. Fractured segments of larger rocks are acceptable. Franchised representatives of the manufacturers of air-type solar systems generally have

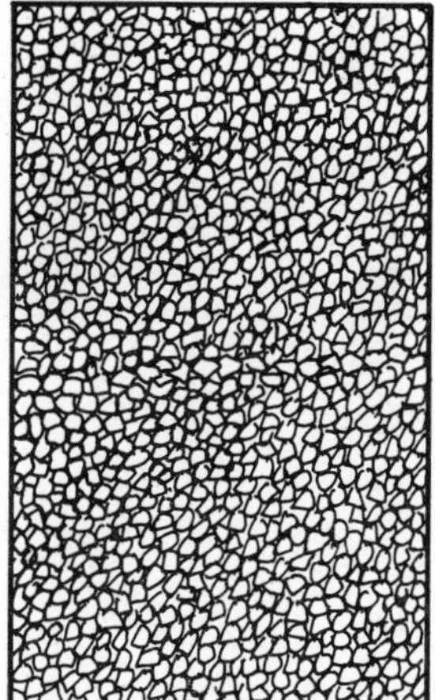

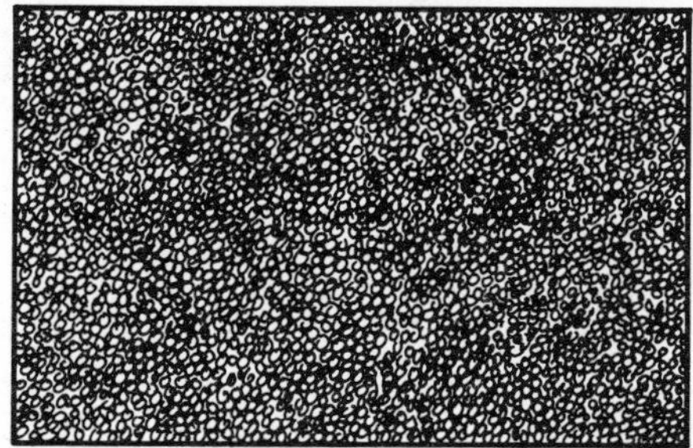

Fig. 6.11 Taller storage bins require rocks of greater diameter; smaller, gravel-like stones (3/4" or more in diameter) are used in lower-profile bins.

access to supplies of suitable rock and can arrange for its delivery to an installation site.

There is a great deal of variation in *size* of rocks that can be employed. A container full of rocks is not, of course, a solid mass of rock. On the average, as much as one-third of the volume held within the bin will consist of air space. It is through this space that the solar-heated air passes as it transmits the heat to the rocks. Small rocks will present more of a surface area over which this heat exchange can take place; larger rocks offer less surface area. Air velocity also affects rock size; a slower air speed becomes more feasible the smaller the size of the rocks. The maximum diameter desirable for storage rocks is generally considered to be 2 inches. An extremely tall, narrow bin (8 to 9 feet or more) may require larger rocks. If air were to be forced over that great a distance through the sizable volume of dead space that 1 or 1½ inch rocks would afford, a more powerful fan would be needed. (See Fig. 6.11.)

Even in more horizontal bins there is a lower limit to the size rocks that can be used. Solaron suggests to its installers that they screen the rocks so that those that pass through a 3/4-inch mesh screen be eliminated.

Along with the collectors themselves, the rock-filled heat storage bin forms the heart of an active air-type solar space heating system. The rest of the equipment is quite conventional (ductwork, blowers, regis-

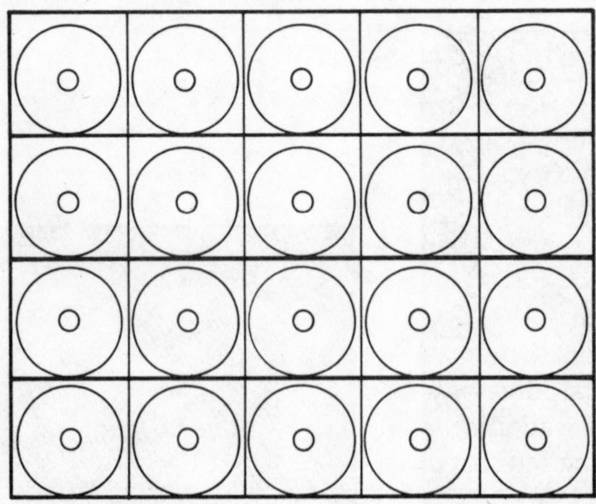

Fig. 6.12 Containers of water can also absorb heat from forced-air circulation.

ters) and will be familiar to anyone who has lived with forced-warm air heat. Before reviewing the details of system sizing, storage capacity, and possible modes of operation, though, it might be interesting to take note of several possible alternatives to storing heat in masses of rock.

Liquid Storage

One alternative to using rock for heat storage is to use water. (See Fig. 6.12.) At first glance the prospect of using solar-heated air to warm a stored supply of water might seem like a classic case of adding apples and oranges. But wait, we are not talking about heating a single large tank of water, such as there is in a liquid-collector domestic hot water or hydronics space heating system. Remember that what counts is *heat transfer*. This can be accomplished in an air-to-water situation just as it is in the water-to-air mode. An air-to-water heat transfer occurs in a liquid-filled exchange coil used to preheat the air in a furnace return duct.

The secret of liquid storage in an installation based on air-type collectors, is the use of numerous small containers of water. Like the rocks in a bin, the individual containers nestle together, not in a solid mass but with intervening spaces through which heated air can circulate. The process of transfer is thus the same as in a rock bin, although the density and thermal storage capacities of these different materials vary and must be taken into consideration when a particular system is designed and sized.

Not only does water require less storage volume than rock, it is easier to use water in irregularly shaped storage areas. Stacked containers of water have been utilized for heat storage within building partitions in some experiments. Bruce Anderson and Michael Riordan in *The Solar Home Book* (see bibliography) suggest the manufacture of specially designed plastic containers that would both stack securely and provide the proper amount of air space between each unit. For now, solar forced-air heat innovators can use makeshift containers such as plastic bleach or milk bottles, metal cans, or even glass jugs. Glass, of course, needs to be handled carefully. Water stored over long periods of time in metal containers should be mixed with a sufficient quantity of an anticorrosive additive.

Until the self-supporting vessels which Anderson and Riordan propose come into common use, experimenters with this type of solar heat storage will have to rely, in most cases, on a custom-built framework that will support the containers and assure that there is sufficient contact

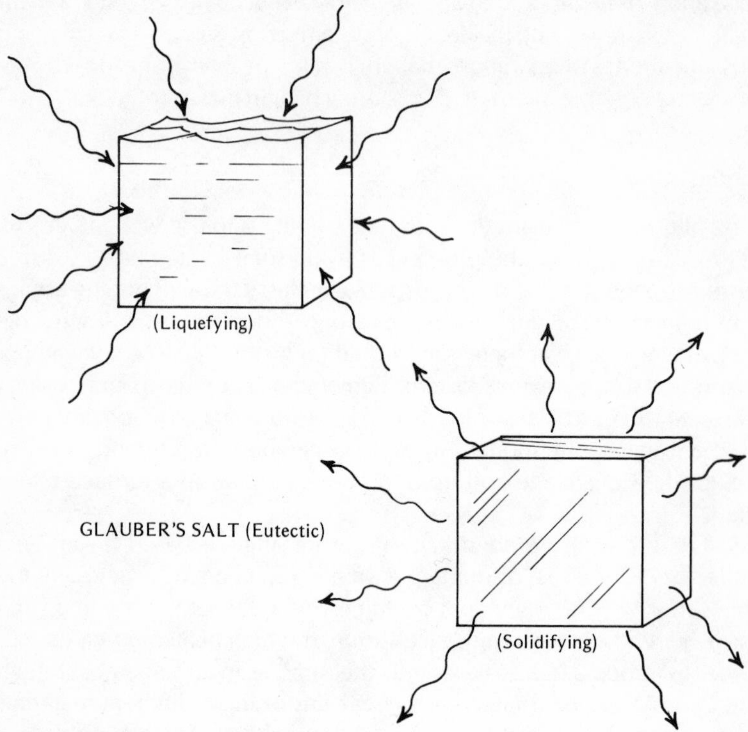

Fig. 6.13 Eutectic salts—of which Glauber's salt is one—store heat as they melt, release it as they solidify.

between heated air and each container. As is true in rock bin storage, the ideal situation is one in which as low-powered a fan as possible can be used to provide the needed air flow. There is no sense in running up electricity expenditures when energy independence is the main idea.

Another promising means of heat storage for forced-air solar space heating is contained in a family of chemicals which have long been known to scientists but which few laymen have heard of. These are the eutectic salts. "Eutectic" refers to their capacity for melting at relatively low temperatures. As with rocks and water storage, the principle of eutectic salt storage is that the contained substance absorbs heat from the air blown past it. This absorbed heat brings the salt to its melting point, generally between 85 and 120°F. The heat is released as the salt solidifies; this in turn warms the cool room air that is ducted through the storage area. (See Fig. 6.13.)

The most commonly used, and the most readily available eutectic salt is a compound called sodium sulfate decahydrate, or Glauber's salt. Two pounds of Glauber's salt can hold as much heat as over a hundred pounds of water when both are heated 1.8°F. However, more of the salts—and more storage space—are needed as the range of storage temperature is increased. The salts have less of an advantage over water, then, if there is a considerable range in the storage temperature. (In *The Solar Home Book* Anderson and Riordan provide a detailed comparison of necessary storage volumes for different temperature ranges.) Providing that production and processing costs can be kept down, the real benefit of the salts may lie in the ease with which they can be located in makeshift storage nooks in solar-heated homes.

Paraffin has qualities similar to those of eutectic salts, although its flammable nature and tendency to expand when heated are likely to prevent its widespread acceptance as a heat storage medium.

SYSTEM SIZE AND STORAGE AREA

It is impossible here to make any generalizations about the size of an air flat-plate collector installation, just as no similar conclusions can be drawn regarding liquid collector systems. The reason, as before, is that climatic differences and individual expectations from a solar energy system vary immeasurably. We can, however, recall that in all except the most ideal climates (i.e., the clear skied southwest), and for all structures except those explicitly designed for solar space heating, it is wiser to strive for a partial rather than a near total solar contribution. (The economics of this decision will be explained in the following chapter on solar payback.)

It is also important to remember that storage capacity must be compatible with the heat-absorbing and circulating potential of the collectors. Forced-air heat distribution does not require as high a storage or circulation temperature as do systems in which hot water runs through radiators; 90 to 120°F will generally suffice. This means that the collectors, while still functioning at the lower, more efficient temperature range, can still provide the needed heat.

The storage capacity must be large enough to store even this relatively "low-grade" heat in sufficient amounts over a reasonable period of time. It is generally agreed that a storage bin (or tank in a liquid system) should be able to receive at least one day's collected heat. Also, most solar installers who want solar energy to contribute part of their heating needs (50–70 percent) prefer that the storage facility be able to provide heat for the duration of one midwinter day or two days in milder seasons when some heat is still demanded.

What these requirements come down to is a prescribed ratio between the storage volume and the collector surface area. The former is expressed in cubic feet, and the latter in square feet. If 60 to 70 percent of a home's heating is to be provided by solar-heated forced air, the ratio generally recommended is between 1/2 to 3/4 cubic feet of rock storage for each square foot of collector surface. It should be noted that there is a point of diminishing returns. Solaron, in its installation guidelines, advises that no advantage is to be gained from storage units sized greater than 3/4 cubic foot per square foot of collector. On the other hand, even though high storage temperatures (if they can be attained) would permit a smaller facility, such a scheme would defeat the advantages of efficient, low-temperature solar collection.

All of these calculations, of course, assume that the proper number of solar collectors have been installed, with a total area matched to the size of the home and the climate of the area. As with any space-heating system, an installer will make these calculations on the basis of the building's heat load.

Another variable, the importance of which cannot be overstressed, is the rate of air flow through the rock bed (or other storage device), and the living areas, and back to the solar collectors. This rate depends on the capacity of the blower used, the size of the ductwork, and the overall dimensions of the storage bin and collectors. The lower the temperature of the air to be distributed, the greater the volume which must be moved in order to afford the desired level of comfort in the living areas of the house. In other words, it is necessary to push more 90°F air than 120°F air in order to provide the same amount of warmth upstairs.

This does not mean that the low-grade heat supplied in an air-type solar system demands a high powered blower in order to get the job done; nearly all home installations of this type make use of a blower with no more than one horsepower capacity. It does mean that the storage bin and the ducts need to be the right dimensions for the proper air flow. There should, then, not be a large pressure drop at the storage bin and the ductwork should be sized to accommodate the prescribed flow of air, generally between 1,000 to 1,500 cubic feet per minute. In other words, these components should be carefully integrated. This presents a strong argument for choosing a system package offered by a single manufacturer, and for choosing a competent installer who can assure that those parts not included in the package still meet the system's specifications.

Domestic Hot Water From an Air-Medium Solar System

Domestic hot water can be provided by a system based on air-type flat-plate solar collectors. The heat exchange here is air-to-water; air returning from the solar collectors heats the domestic storage supply. Once again, circulation of water through a heat-exchange coil makes the transfer possible.

In a typical installation solar-heated air is ducted from the collectors to an insulated module containing the coil. (There has also been some success with coils located right in the rock bins in homes where space heating is also supplied by air-type collectors.) A blower, sized to match the collector area and the home's hot water storage capability, assures a steady flow of air. Meanwhile, a circulator pump cycles water through the coil and returns it to the storage tank.

As with systems in which liquid-type collectors supply the heat, the circulation of water automatically stops when the water in the tank has been heated to a preset temperature (usually 150–160°F) or when solar collection conditions make it impossible for the tank water to be heated further—in other words, when the gap between collector temperature and storage temperature has been closed. Like the all-liquid domestic hot water installations described earlier in this book, a system based on an air-to-water heat exchange is frequently quite capable of providing tap water that requires no further heating after it leaves the solar storage tank. The occasional need for auxiliary heating can be met by a secondary tank that is equipped with gas burners or electric elements and receives solar preheated water from the primary tank, or simply by the use of a thermostatically controlled electric element within the solar tank itself.

Air-type space heating systems can be designed to accommodate the domestic hot water heat exchange units, or the water heaters may be installed independently of an existing conventional heating plant. The blower coil assembly (even though insulated) should ideally be located in a heated portion of the house, regardless of whether or not it is part of a larger space-heating arrangement.

Air-Type Space Heating: Modes of Operation

A space heating system incorporating air-type flat-plate collectors and a rock bin or other thermal mass as a heat storage facility lends itself to several modes of operation, as well as assorted options for back-up heating. (See Fig. 6.14.)

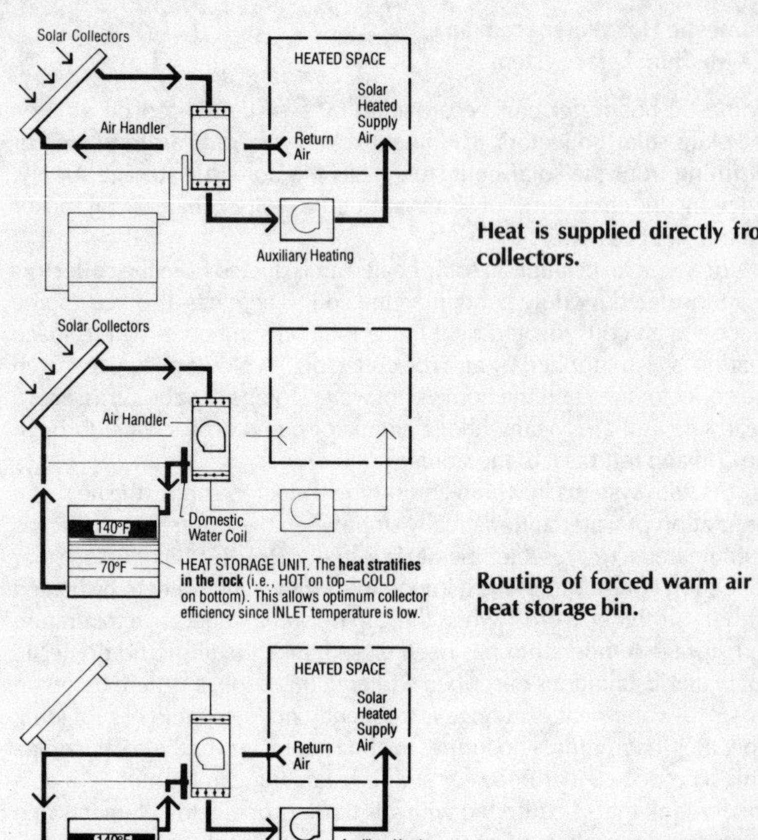

Heat is supplied directly from collectors.

Routing of forced warm air to heat storage bin.

Space is heated from storage when solar collection is not feasible.

Fig. 6.14 Three modes of heating with an air-type system. (Courtesy Solaron Corp.)

Both the collectors and the heat distribution system in this type of solar installation rely on the same medium—air. Large volumes of heated air can be cycled into the building's living area by means of the same blower that serves the collectors. During cold but sunny weather, air-type systems operate by direct heating from the collectors. Forced-air enters the rooms of the house in the same way as would air warmed in a conventional furnace. The air supply comes straight from the collectors while the return duct carries cool room air back to the collectors.

During the course of the day, as heat provided by the collectors surpasses the amount needed for maintaining comfort in the house, the excess is channeled into the storage bin. The heat stratification principle applies to rock as well as water; the warm air is ducted to the top of the bin, while the duct leading back to the collectors exits the bin from the cooler bottom portion. This assures more efficient collector operation. If a coil or tank imbedded in the storage bin (rather than a duct coil) is employed, it is at this point that the domestic water supply is heated.

The next phase of the system's operation occurs during cloudy periods, or at night, when direct heating from the collectors is not feasible. During such periods a separate blower (or the main air handler in a modular system) cycles air between the rooms and the storage bin, bypassing the ducts leading to the collectors. Warm air is drawn from the upper, higher-temperature strata of the storage bin, and recycled, via the return duct from the rooms, into the lower level. In this way, the air reheats as it rises through the layers of rock into the warmer strata above where the process begins again.

Obviously, a prolonged period of cloudy weather will exhaust the heat supply stored within the rock bin or other facility. The length of time it takes for this to occur depends on the storage capacity and the requirements of the house. The time period is calculated at the time the system is installed.

This is where auxiliary heating comes in. A completely separate heat source and delivery system might seem to be the simplest solution, but there is no reason why the auxiliary system should not be integrated with the solar facility—except, perhaps, in a small house where a wood stove or gravity hot air system can meet all heating needs. The function of the auxiliary system (gas, oil, multifuel, or electric furnace) is twofold. When the heat contained in the storage bin is insufficient, the auxiliary burner can draw air through the bin, bring it up to the required temperature, and circulate it through the house. In this situation, the storage bin is serving as a source of preheated air, and as such helps cut the amount of energy used by the conventional auxiliary device. Should all of the stored heat be exhausted, the bin is bypassed and the auxiliary heater performs the full task. There is nothing to be accomplished by having the conventional unit heat the storage bin; thermostatic dampers in sophisticated systems of this type assure that this will not take place. When the sun shines, of course, the ducts leading from collectors to storage are automatically opened, and the process of reheating the storage material begins.

The heat pump can also play a role in this type of installation. If a heat pump is installed as the auxiliary heating system, it can use warm air from the storage bin as its heat source, thus taking advantage of solar collection even on days when it would be insufficient to meet direct heating needs. When necessary, of course, the heat pump can rely upon its own electric backup feature.

One of the encouraging aspects of air-type solar collection and heat distribution systems is their potential, in some areas, for use as cooling as well as heating devices. We will take a closer look at how this can be accomplished in the sections on active and passive solar cooling later in this book.

Chapter 7

PAYBACK

Earlier in this book, reference was made to the concept of "payback." Payback is the ability of a solar hot water or space heating system to return its original cost to its owner by saving conventional fuel. Having examined the more practical and popular applications of active solar heating, it might be helpful for us to look further into the payback idea and the way in which solar savings are computed.

In a very real sense, the notion of payback as applied to domestic solar installations is inherently unfair. In most people's minds, a quick payback on a home solar investment is equivalent to a justification of the technology. Yet what other types of equipment are subjected to this criterion? If you buy a gas-fired water heater, it will indeed be cheaper than a solar domestic hot water installation, especially since the solar equipment still requires some form of backup heat which may or may not already be in place. But at what point could the gas heater be said to have paid for itself? The answer, of course, is never. Any appliance which requires a perpetual supply of a commodity such as gas, oil, or electricity will never come to the end of its "payback period." Such a heater will not pay back unless the fuel which it uses is significantly cheaper than that which was used before, thus allowing the savings eventually to equal the sum spent on the new equipment's purchase.

Appliances which make use of solar energy are the best example of this sort of investment return. During a good part of their operation solar appliances do not merely substitute a cheaper fuel but substitute the free power of the sun. It is no doubt because of this dramatic prospect of being truly able to "pay for themselves" that solar hot water and space heating systems are subjected to the notion of payback.

There are several simple steps in calculating the payback time of a solar installation. A qualified installer, particularly if he regularly represents one of the leading system manufacturers should be able to assist you in arriving at a reasonably close estimate.

The first step is to figure the amount of money that you spend each year to provide the service—hot water or space heating—for which the solar assist is planned. Your calculation will be based on fuel or utility rates, the amount of service required, and the fuel or electricity consumption rate of the equipment currently used. All of these factors will be reflected in preceding years' bills for these commodities. Therefore, if you are seriously thinking about installing solar equipment, you should be sure to save all such invoices. After the solar system is in place, you will want to save fuel bills so that you can tally up your savings.

As you add up past expenses, do not forget to take into account the rate at which unit costs have risen. Everyone has fond memories of what fuels and electricity used to cost. This writer remembers paying $.14 a gallon for number two heating oil in Vermont in 1971 and $.85 a gallon in Massachusetts in the summer of 1979. By the time these words are printed even the latter figure will no doubt be a happy recollection.

The inflation rate, then, is an important part of payback calculations. If the potential installer wishes to figure increases on a yearly basis, it is likely that his or her figures will show a 10 to 15 percent annual increase in home energy costs over the past 10 years, depending upon the location of the home and the type, source, and availability of the fuel used. It would certainly not be rash to estimate at least a 10 percent annual increase in future energy costs. If anything, this may be a conservative estimate. The homeowner calculating potential solar payback is more likely to err by underestimating energy expenditures in the years to come rather than by overestimating them.

The next step in computing payback is to add up the total cost of the planned solar installation including equipment, labor, and whatever modifications are to be made on the home. If a new conventional backup system is to be installed, or—in the case of space heating—the solar addition is part of a major energy conservation program (including insulation, weather stripping, and related "tightening up" procedures), the homeowner may wish to include savings resulting from the solar contribution as part of the general benefits afforded by energy-wise remodeling. He would likewise total all related initial expenditures, otherwise, it might be difficult to isolate the portion of the savings for which the solar conversion is responsible.

The next phase of the payback tally is a bit more complicated. It involves making a fair estimate of the total contribution solar energy will make toward performing the required tasks during the course of an average year. This figure will be represented as a percentage of the total energy costs. The figure will be greatly influenced by the efficiency of the equipment selected, the collector area, and the angle at which it faces the sun, as well as by the insolation and percentage of possible sunshine in your area, and the storage capacity envisioned. Here is where the assistance of a competent installer can be invaluable. This individual should be willing to assess your situation and provide these estimates for a modest fee. You will have to cooperate, of course, by providing information on your household's rate of hot water consumption or, for space heating systems, the building's heat load and the presence or absence of insulation. For new homes, an architect or solar designer should be able to provide similar information.

Here is a good point at which to recall the problems inherent in striving for too great a percentage of solar contribution to the home's energy requirements. The closer you come to getting 100 percent of your energy requirements from an active solar system, the more the intial cost multiplies. The reason for this is that the collector area and the storage system both become very extensive. Homes in which energy requirements are met completely by active solar systems do exist, but they are either located in ideal climates or have been built or retrofitted for the purpose of proving technologies rather than providing short-term savings. The more a solar installation costs relative to previous conventional energy expenditures, the longer its payback period will be: it is as simple as that.

On the other hand, it is unwise to install an undersized solar system, one that will be responsible for too small a part of a home's hot water or space heating needs. Once again, the reason is economic: if you are going to spend the money, why not spend a little more and get a greater portion of the job done?

The optimum payback periods, then, will be afforded by systems that attempt to do neither too much nor too little of the heating job at hand. That is why the first step in changing to solar energy is to take time with your paperwork.

After you have arrived at the percentage the solar system will contribute to your energy requirements, you need to put this figure into a dollar amount. You already know how much you spend per year on oil, gas, or electricity, and you should have a good idea just how much you use. Multiply the solar percentage times the amount spent on energy per year to come up with your estimated annual savings. (If you are only installing a solar domestic water heater and have previously made use of an integrated system that uses conventional fuels to provide both space heat and hot water, remember that the solar part of the energy expenditure will be smaller than if it simply reflected fuel saved in hot water heating.)

Now you are ready to estimate the payback period. To do this, divide the anticipated annual savings into the total cost of the solar installation. The resulting figure will equal the number of years that must pass before the new system has paid for itself, and can actually begin to save you money.

There are other cost factors that can influence the length of the payback period, although none of them is as important as the basic steps outlined above. One is the idea of "life-cycle costing." The life-cycle cost is an estimate of all anticipated expenditures related to a new purchase over the lifetime of the equipment being purchased. The estimated expenditure is then added to the initial cost to reveal the actual cash outlay that the new purchase demands. As an example (although one for which the payback idea does not apply), let us consider the automobile. If a car costs $6,000, and the parts and repairs which it needs during five years of ownership cost another $2,000, then the overall, *life-cycle* cost of the car is $8,000. Not counting fuel and insurance, then, the vehicle will cost its owner $1600 a year over this period.

An active solar system also requires maintenance, although fortunately not nearly so much as an automobile. You will want a service technician to inspect the equipment every couple of years. In a closed-loop domestic hot water system there will be a routine replacement of the heat-transfer antifreeze fluid as described in Chapter 5. Repair of pumps and blowers is infrequent, although discussions with installers and with people who already own systems similar to the one you are considering will help you evaluate the potential for expenditures in this area over the 15 or 20 year period for which you are making your calculations. (This is not intended to represent the actual life span of a solar installation, but is merely a figure agreed upon by many analysts as a basis for figuring life-cycle costs. Actually, most systems have yet to attain this age since home solar technology is such a recent development.)

Other costs to add in when calculating the payback period are the cost of electricity to run pumps and/or blowers, and the interest on a bank loan should one be necessary for the initial purchase. Contrary to many people's belief, banks are becoming much more agreeable to the idea of lending money for solar conversions provided that the usual requirements for loan approval are met.

Now that you have added these secondary expenditures to the cost of a planned solar installation, do not forget the similar hidden costs that apply to conventional equipment. Gas and oil burners also require maintenance and also make use of electricity to power mechanical heat-distribution equipment. Lenders also charge interest on money borrowed for the purchase of conventional devices.

Finally, it is important—and gratifying—to consider some of the real financial incentives for solar conversion. The first is the federal income tax credit provided for in the National Energy Act. The credit allowed purchasers of new home solar energy installations is 30 percent of the first $2,000 and 20 percent of the next $8,000 spent on the equipment. This is not a deduction to be taken against taxable income, but a sum which may be subtracted directly from taxes owed the federal government. For most taxpayers, this would mean the equivalent of a $600 saving on a system costing $2,000. As of this writing some states have passed, and several others are considering, similar solar tax credits.

In 1977, the U. S. Department of Health, Education, and Welfare (HUD) launched a program offering $400 direct grants to purchasers of approved solar domestic hot water systems. The grants have been administered on a state-by-state basis, and although all funds appropriated for the program have been disbursed in some states, other states may still be accepting grant applications. For information on whether your state is a current participant, contact HUD or your state energy or consumer affairs office.

Taken together, the tax credits and HUD grants have significantly reduced the cost of solar conversion and have cut payback periods for a great many homeowners. One of the best advantages of a solar hot water or space heating system is not realized until later when the house is sold. Not only are resale values already higher for homes which have a proven record of energy-saving solar assistance, but they are sure to rise along with the prices of conventional fuels. This may turn out to be the nicest "payback" of all.

SOLAR PAYBACK: ONE EXAMPLE

Here is an illustration of the way in which the payback period can work. This hypothetical case compares the cost of a solar domes-

needs. The remainder of Jones's water heating will be done by electricity, purchased at the same rate paid by Smith.

Let us assume that electricity costs $.06 per kilowatt hour at the time the two systems are installed with a 10 percent rate of inflation projected. At the end of 15 years, based on the consumption of 5900 kilowatt hours per year, Smith will have paid $11,175 for electricity to heat his hot water. Jones, who derives half of his energy to heat water from solar energy, will have spent $5,587.50—half of the above amount. Using the inflation adjusted scale, we can estimate that Jones will have saved nearly $2600 in the first 9½ years of his solar heater's operation. In other words, the solar equipment will have paid for itself in a payback period of 9½ years. In years to come, as electricity rates continue to climb, his savings will be even greater. Had he installed a solar heater capable of supplying more than 50 percent of his hot water needs, a feat which is not at all difficult in most climates, the payback period would have been proportionately shorter. Tax advantages brighten the picture even more, as does the improved resale value of Jones's house. (See Fig. 7.1.)

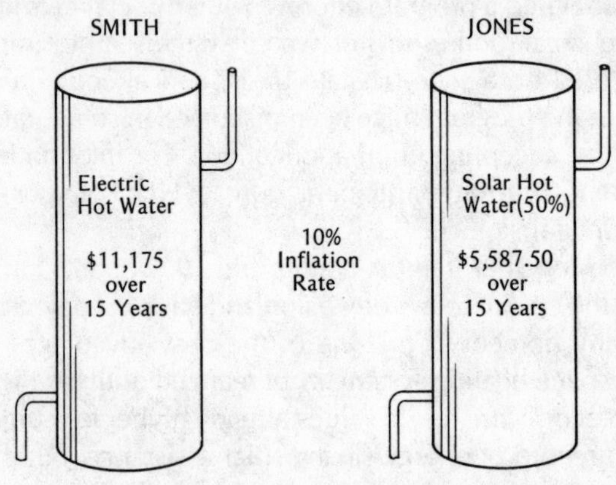

Fig. 7.1 Smith-Jones payback chart.

Chapter 8

SOLAR HEATING OF A SWIMMING POOL

No one can deny that the domestic hot water and space heating applications of solar energy are far more important than such secondary uses as heating water for swimming pools. Yet according to a 1979 estimate, some 80,000 to 90,000 home pools are installed each year in the United States, and many of the owners of these pools have turned to various heating systems in order to achieve a longer swimming season. This is understandable; pools are not cheap, and anyone paying to build one will want to get as much use out of it as possible.

Rising energy costs and the scarcity of energy sources, have made it more difficult to justify this type of expenditure, either on economic or social grounds. That is why an increasing number of new pools (over 50,000, as of 1979) are heated by solar energy. In fact, several states have passed laws which make it illegal to heat new pools by any other means.

Solar pool heating is nothing new. Any natural body of water or an unheated pool warm enough to swim in has gotten that way because of its absorption of heat from the sun. The modern applications of solar technology merely hasten this process by circulating the water through collectors. Heat retention is assisted, in many cases, by the use of an easily removable translucent or transparent plastic cover. Not only can solar pool heating stretch the summer, in warmer climates it can even make comfortable year-round swimming possible. When compared with conventional means of warming pool water, it affords a payback schedule that is among the most attractive of any solar appliances.

Like indoor hot water and space heating, solar pool heating is based on the flat-plate collector. The different requirements of an outdoor installation that is generally intended for use only during milder weather have led designers to come up with collectors that differ somewhat from the types discussed earlier in this book. Fortunately, most of these special design criteria have resulted in the pool collectors being less expensive than their space heating and domestic hot water counterparts.

To begin with, a flat-plate collector for a swimming pool need not provide high-grade heat, nor must it contend with extremely low outdoor temperatures during the time when it is in operation. These are the main factors that increase design flexibility in pool-heating collectors. Air temperatures during the pool season are rarely more than 10 to 20°F lower than the temperature desired for the pool. On a typical spring or fall day the collectors might be required to provide 75 or 80°F water when the ambient outdoor temperature is 68°F.

As we saw earlier, the lower the temperature at which a flat-plate collector operates, the greater its efficiency is likely to be. Within this operating range conduction and convection heat loss from the collector are minimal. Thus it is possible to dispense with two of the principal features of the conventional collector: glazing and insulation. (See Fig. 8.1.) Glazed and insulated collectors can be used effectively for pool

Fig. 8.1 Collectors used in pool system are often simpler in construction than conventional flat-plate designs. (Courtesy Solar Solutions/Peter Southwick, photographer.)

heating, but they are generally chosen only when the system is intended to serve a space heating purpose as well. for pool heating alone, glazed collectors will actually prove less efficient than the unglazed variety during most of the operating season.

The typical pool collector, then, has a much lower profile, is much lighter, and is cheaper and easier to produce than the standard models. Another cost-saving innovation that can be used in the application of solar energy to swimming pool heating is the use of flexible plastics for the absorber plates and tubing in these collectors. (A collector designed exclusively for pool heating is, in effect, little more than an absorber plate and tubing along with the necessary headers and connection lines to the other collectors in the array.) Plastic is an especially useful material for this type of collector in view of the fact that the water that must be cycled through the tubing is treated with chemicals that might easily corrode some unprotected metals. Not all plastics, of course, are altogether impervious to these substances or to the heat, ultraviolet light, and other stresses which they will encounter in regular service. The better manufacturers of pool-heating collectors use exposure- and corrosion-resistant polymer compounds or ABS plastics (acrylonitrile-butadiene styrene) treated with carbon black or other ultraviolet degradation inhibitors. (See Fig. 8.2.)

The less stringent operating requirements of pool heating systems also permit some relaxation of the standards regularly observed in locating, angling, and orienting collectors. This is not to say that the basic requirement of a southerly or near-southerly orientation can be ignored, but that a slight deviation from the norm will result in less of a corresponding decline in efficiency.

As with installations designed for indoor heating, whatever efficiency loss does occur can be offset by an increase in collector area. (Depending on climate and collector efficiency, most manufacturers recommend that the collector surface take up an area equivalent to between 50 and 75 percent of the pool surface.) The summer sun is high enough for the collectors to absorb sufficient heat for the pool even when efficiency is less than optimal. Therefore, during the May-to-September period the sun's rays need not strike the collectors at a perfect right angle, and supplementary bracketing for collector installations on a low-pitched roof should not be necessary.

When the pool owner expects satisfactory service from his system earlier in the spring or later in the fall, it becomes more important to follow some sloping criteria. Once again, the installation's latitude becomes a factor. The recommendation for determining collector tilt is

Fig. 8.2a Solar collectors designed by Solar Industries of Farmingdale, New Jersey, can be mounted on available roof space or on ground supports. This photograph shows an array of collectors mounted directly to earthen banks.

Fig. 8.2b Black polypropylene solar collectors from Solar Industries, originally designed for swimming pools, are now also being used to heat hot tubs and spas.

to use an angle equivalent to the site latitude minus 10 degrees as the base figure (for summer operation), and to increase the angle's steepness up to 20 degrees (to a maximum of latitude plus 10) in order to achieve greater comfort in the spring and fall.

In cold climates the usefulness of even a perfectly oriented and angled collector array will taper off toward winter simply because the air temperature is low and the pool has a tendency to lose heat despite the performance of the collectors. As a means of storing heat a swimming pool, despite its mass, will never compare with a heavily insulated rock bin or water storage tank.

If you feel that a bathing suit is adequate protection against the cold, and that clear-day solar collection makes your pool warm enough for winter swimming, you will have to take some precaution to prevent nighttime or cloudy-day freezing within the collectors. Since no one likes to swim in propylene glycol, this will have to take the form of a drain-back system, with the accompanying valves and temperature sensors.

The actual operation of a solar-heated pool is quite simple. Pool water is pumped through the collectors usually at the rate of 2 to 5 gallons per minute per panel. It is important that the manufacturer's prescribed flow rate be maintained. Too fast a circulation of water means that not enough heat will be absorbed. If the rate is too slow, the collectors will operate at too high a temperature, and the resulting heat loss will reduce overall efficiency.

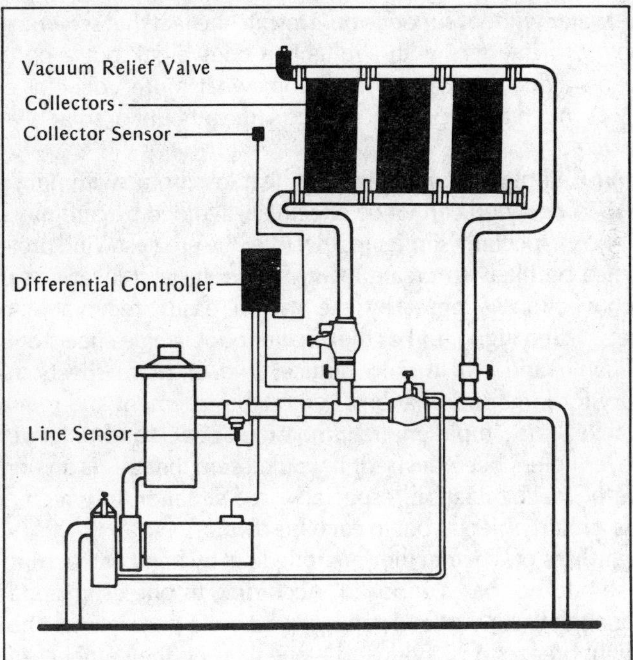

Fig. 8.3 Diagram shows functioning of typical solar swimming pool heating system. (Courtesy Solar Solutions.)

As with any liquid-based solar collection installation, it is the temperature difference between the storage facility (in this case, the pool) and the collectors that determines whether circulation is to continue. When the gap has closed sufficiently, the pump is automatically turned off. In one typical double-sensor installation, circulation begins when there is a 3°F difference and stops when only 1°F separates the temperatures of pool and collectors. (See Fig. 8.3.)

CONSERVING POOL HEAT

There are two basic ways to conserve the heat stored in a pool by a solar installation. The first is a precautionary measure and consists simply of the proper location of the pool. Pool water will stay warm longer if it can receive direct sunshine; even if the collectors are located in an unshaded area, heat will dissipate from the water if the pool itself lies in the shadow of buildings or trees. Another shade producer is the screened pool enclosure, which is sometimes installed as a means of keeping out insects, or for protecting small children who might stray near the water without supervision. Despite the fact that screening does not appear to interfere with sunlight, it does block out a portion of it. Screen-shaded pools thus need somewhat more collector area—possibly as much as 25 percent—if the same amount of solar heating is to be realized.

Wind is another major source of heat loss from swimming pools. Unlike shading, wind cannot be effectively avoided by carefully situating the pool, especially since sites that offer the greatest wind protection would also be likely to create heavy shade. Instead, heat loss due to wind convection is offset by the use of easily removable plastic "blankets." (See Fig. 8.4.) For the smaller pool, single sheets of plastic are available and will usually suffice; two or more sheets may be necessary for larger installations. Although placement and removal of the "blankets" is simple enough, motorized, track-and-roller versions have nevertheless been devised. It would seem that this is an unnecessary use of mechanization, especially in a situation in which energy saving is a main object—but to each his own.

Regardless of whether they are rolled out by hand or machine, pool covers should not be overlooked. According to one estimate, a wind strong enough to stir dust and paper can cause 15 percent more heat loss than a light breeze. A higher wind—one that sets the branches of small trees in motion—can raise this figure to 30 percent. Especially in the spring and fall, plastic pool coverings can cut this loss significantly. The

Fig. 8.4 A pool cover (as shown here on a demonstration model) can help capture direct solar gain as well as conserve heat provided via active collectors. (Courtesy Löf Brothers Solar Appliances.)

covers are also useful at night and during cloudy periods, when solar collection is not taking place and it becomes important to conserve whatever heat is stored in the pool. And, of course, they will keep leaves and debris out of the water.

It is possible, by using translucent plastic pool covers, to create a "greenhouse effect" within the pool itself and thereby assist the active solar system by providing passive heat gain. If this is the object, it makes sense to leave the cover in place even on warm or windless days when the pool is not in use.

There is a point at which pool water, because of direct solar heat gain, can become warmer than a swimmer might prefer. This is likely to be a problem only in more southerly climates and only in the dead of summer. Some solar pool heating systems are designed so that their primary function can be reversed and cooling of the pool water provided. There is no real trick to this; all it involves is the circulation of water through the collectors at night instead of during the day. All that is required, aside from the basic solar pool hardware, is for the system's sensors and controls to be set to respond to the correct temperature differences. A marked difference in the day and night outdoor temperatures, such as occurs in the American Southwest, is also helpful.

THE ROLE OF THE POOL IN A SOLAR-ASSISTED HEAT PUMP INSTALLATION

A heat pump, you will recall, depends for its operation on a heat *source* and a heat *sink*. When its mode of operation is reversed for summer air-conditioning, the roles of heat source and sink are similarly turned around.

In the solar-assisted heat pump installations that we looked at earlier, the winter heat source is the solar storage tank. Under most circumstances the solar storage tank is able to provide usable heat to the pump even when its temperatures are too low to make direct solar heating possible. In summer the heat source is the house itself, and the heat sink (the place where excess heat is "dumped") is the outdoors. The presence of a solar-heated swimming pool can provide an interesting variation to this arrangement.

In mild climates where winter temperatures below 32°F are uncommon, it is possible for a liquid-to-liquid or liquid-to-air heat pump to make use of a solar-heated pool as its heat source. The collectors heat the pool water, and the heat pump, in turn, draws upon this heat and transfers it to the house. As long as the temperature of the water stays sufficiently high for efficient heat pump operation (at least 45–50°F), there is no need for constant solar collection. Even during short periods when the collectors are unable to function effectively, it is likely that the large liquid volume of the pool will continue to be a usable source of heat. When this heat is depleted, the heat pump's electric assist will take over.

When air conditioning is the object, a heat pump operating in the liquid-to-liquid or air-to-liquid mode can use the swimming pool as its heat sink instead. Heat drawn from the house is simply "dumped" into the pool where it is more welcome. Again, it should be remembered that the benefits of heat pump ownership, particularly if a pool is involved, are proportionately greater in areas where winters are mild. Usefulness as an air conditioner also goes a long way toward justifying the installation of one of these machines.

Chapter 9

SOLAR COOLING

Most people are reasonably receptive to the idea of solar heating since the warmth of the sun is something that everyone has experienced. Only the methods of collection and storage need to be explained. Solar cooling, however, is an idea that at first glance seems to make no sense at all. How can such a paradox actually work?

The answer begins to come into focus when we remember that the sun is not merely a source of heat, but also of energy. We are all familiar with heat energy as a source of power for end-use applications unrelated to heating; our home appliances, for example, are driven by electricity generated through enormous expenditures of heat. It is logical, then, that solar heat energy should be able to perform varieties of jobs not directly related to raising the temperature of a living space or water supply. One of these jobs is cooling; the equipment with which to do it is well along in its testing and early production phase, as we shall see later in this chapter.

First, though, we should turn our attention to the means by which active air-type solar heating systems can be used for cooling. This is a much less expensive application of solar technology to summer indoor climate control, and one that coupled as it is with heating capacity, can greatly improve the payback potential of the equipment involved.

You will recall that an air-type system incorporates two major features: the collectors and the storage bin. The key to understanding how this type of installation can cool as well as heat a house is to remember that the storage facility constitutes a thermal mass, capable of storing heat *at whatever temperature it receives it*. Just as air circulating through solar collectors can be heated to 110°F, it can also be heated to 65 or 70°F. Blow this air into a rock bin, and the rocks will retain and release this lower-grade heat.

During the winter, the time to operate a solar collection system is during the day when the most heat is available. In the summer, when cooling is desired, the circulation of air through the collectors and past the storage mass should take place at night, unless, of course, conditions are such that there is no significant difference between daytime and nighttime temperatures. Fortunately, in many parts of North America, there is a substantial drop in temperature after the summer sun has set.

After the storage medium has been cooled by this nighttime air circulation, the next step is to circulate the house air through the storage bin during the warmer hours of the day. Naturally, the ducts leading to and from the collectors are dampered during this phase of operation. Air from the house gives up heat to the rocks (or other storage medium) as it passes through the bin; it is thus "chilled" by the time it is recycled into living areas. If this cooling mode is to be employed, system capacity for coolness storage should be gauged at the time of installation and the necessary modifications made in the distribution hardware.

In situations where outdoor nighttime temperatures are too high to allow the collectors to supply sufficiently cool air to the storage system, there has been some success with using a conventional, electrically-powered air conditioner to chill the rocks during the night. Daytime circulation of cool air from the rock storage to the house is accomplished entirely by the solar system's air handler. This procedure makes sense if the house is located in an area where electric rates are lower during "off-peak" hours when power demand is lowest. Even if the same rates apply day and night, however, it constitutes something of a public service to avoid the operation of so heavy a power consumer as an air conditioner during peak afternoon hours. The increasing number of summer "brownouts" bears out this idea.

A similar, although even simpler, adaptation of an air-type installation to summer cooling can be accomplished if the system's rock storage bin is situated so that it can release heat, without the use of a blower, into the night air. (See Fig. 9.1.) The method used is to close the damper which leads from storage into the home, and to open another, leading directly to the outdoors. During the day, the procedure is reversed, and room air is circulated through the storage bin by means of the system's blower. Since heat travels from warmer to cooler substances, the air yields its warmth to the rocks before returning to the living areas. The rocks, meanwhile, store the heat which they will release when the process is repeated after nightfall.

The collectors, rather than the storage facility, play an important part in another proven cooling scheme. This cooling method is a varia-

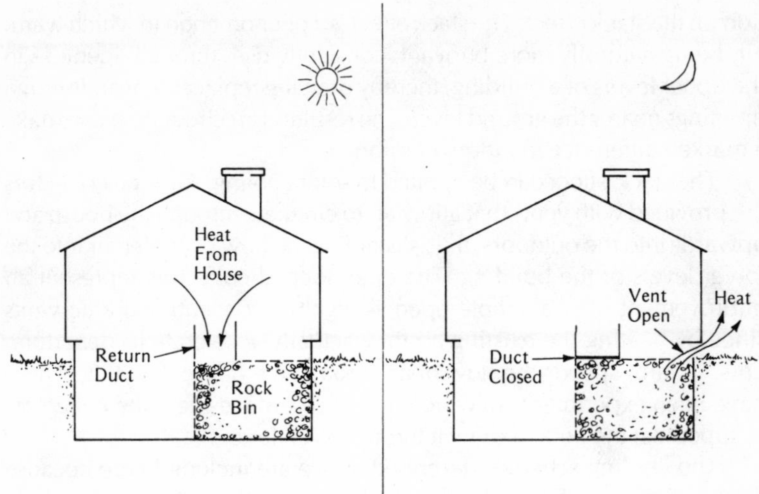

Fig. 9.1 An air-type system can be used for cooling as well as heating, if the storage mass can be effectively exposed to outdoor air at night.

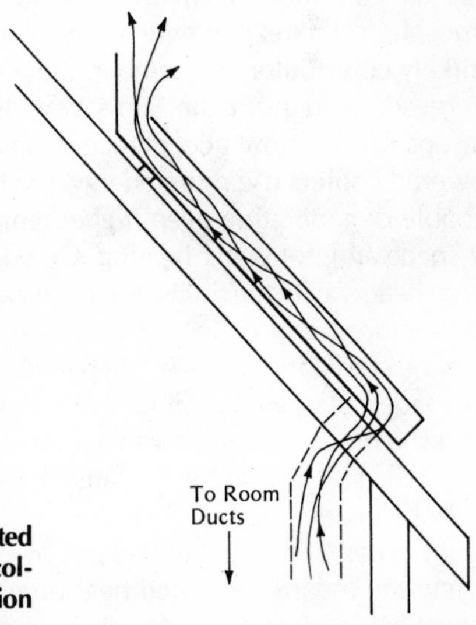

Fig. 9.2 A convection draft is created by the heating of air in vented collectors, thus speeding circulation throughout the house.

tion on the stack effect. The stack effect is a phenomenon in which warm air, being naturally more buoyant, constantly rises through openings in the upper levels of a building, thereby drawing replacement air through openings nearer the ground level. The resulting air circulation can make a marked difference in indoor comfort.

The stack effect can be applied to solar cooling. Air-type collectors are provided with vents that allow air to circulate through the house and upwards into the outdoors, thus sustaining the flow of cooler air into the lower levels of the building. The open-topped collectors represent an improvement over a simple open skylight or conventional attic vents since by heating the existing air they actually accelerate its departure. This, in turn, speeds the flow of air through the house (Fig. 9.2.) There have been experiments in which reflective surfaces help the collectors to superheat the air and draw it through even faster.

The cooling schemes described above are included here because they make use of the hardware necessary for active solar heating. Even simpler, less mechanically dependent means of providing warm weather comfort are discussed in the following chapter on passive solar applications.

SOLAR AIR CONDITIONING

True air conditioning involves the actual refrigeration of the indoor atmosphere. Here is where solar energy seems to be an especially unlikely contributor. Remember, though, that we are talking about the *energy* derived from the sun's warmth. Oddly enough, one of the reasons for the slow acceptance of solar air conditioning is that sun-powered coolers use more energy and must actually rely on collectors capable of generating even *higher* temperatures than those necessary for space and hot water heating. Only recently have researchers made much headway in the dual effort of designing coolers that "fire" at lower temperatures, and collectors that can supply greater amounts of heat than the conventional flat-plate panels. Although these efforts have not yet made solar air conditioning the system of first resort, modular domestic models (usually with a 3-ton capacity) have already appeared (Fig. 9.3), and a number of large-scale commercial installations are currently in operation.

In order to understand solar-powered cooling, it is necessary to review the means by which heat pumps and conventional air conditioners achieve climate control. Both of these devices rely on a con-

Fig. 9.3 This is the Arkla Solaire 36P packaged solar-powered absorption chiller. It also supplies space and domestic hot water heating. The air conditioning unit has a 3-ton (36,000 Btu) capacity. (Courtesy Arkla Industries.)

tinuous cycle of evaporation and condensation of a volatile fluid. (Despite common usage, "volatile" in the strict chemical sense does not mean "explosive," but rather it is used to describe fluids that evaporate at a relatively low temperature.) When such a fluid (in this case, it is usually called a *refrigerant*) evaporates, it becomes capable of absorbing heat from its surroundings. When the fluid condenses, it releases this stored heat. This process of evaporation and condensation of a volatile fluid, you may observe, is similar to the process that makes eutectic salts an effective storage medium for an air-type solar heating system. The salts are not truly volatile; they simply melt rather than evaporate. Also, their cycle takes place over a much longer period of time.

In a heat pump or air conditioner, the condensation-vaporization cycle is accelerated by mechanical means. A compressor, powered by electricity, squeezes the hot, gaseous refrigerant back into liquid form. Then the heat it has absorbed indoors is released through radiation from the coils on the outside of the building. The cool fluid is now ready to begin the absorption process over again.

This cycling between two phases of a volatile liquid is also the essential operating principle in a solar-powered air conditioner—a machine generally referred to as an "absorption chiller." (See Fig. 9.4.) Electricity, however, plays not nearly as large and expensive a role in the solar units; it is needed only to power a small circulating pump rather than a high-powered compressor motor.

Where does the sun fit in? In an absorption chiller the refrigerant (formerly ammonia but now usually lithium bromide) is held in solution with water. Solar collectors heat a separate liquid, which is circulated through a heat exchange coil. The coil is located within the container (called the "generator") that holds the refrigerant-water solution. In most chillers this fluid heated in the collectors is water. If the solar-heated fluid is water, there will have to be a draindown system into a separate storage tank to allow for cold weather.

When the lithium bromide-water mixture is heated by the solar exchange coil, the lithium bromide separates from the water with which it is in solution. The lithium bromide evaporates out of the solution and condenses separately in a different receptacle. Next, after it has been

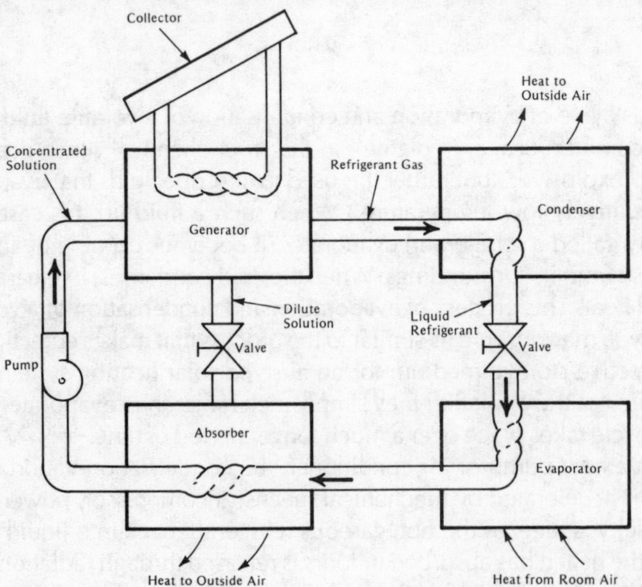

Fig. 9.4 The basic cycle employed in a solar-powered absorption chiller.

transformed back into a vapor by accumulating this room heat, the lithium bromide condenses into a liquid. In its liquid state the undiluted refrigerant (the lithium bromide) is able to absorb room heat and cool the room as it travels through the evaporator coil. The lithium bromide is then reabsorbed into the water solution and in the process, gives off heat to the outside. With the assistance of the small electric pump mentioned above, the cycle begins anew.

As you can readily see, the successful operation of this system depends on the ability of the solar collectors to provide sufficient heat for the evaporation of the refrigerant out of its water solution. One of the strong points of the absorption chiller is that the times at which solar collection are best are also the times when air conditioning is most in demand. Denis Hayes points out in his Worldwatch paper, *Energy: The Solar Prospect*, that the use of solar-powered cooling devices during these periods could help reduce peak loads on electrical power grids.

As was noted above, however, the fact that the absorption chillers demand such high-grade heat has been one of their main drawbacks to date. In any chiller there is a bottom limit to the temperature beyond which the evaporative process cannot take place effectively. For most units this temperature has been well in excess of 200°F and sometimes

Fig. 9.5 The evacuated tube collector, in which the heat transfer fluid circulates through tubes surrounded by vacuum space. This type of collector is capable of generating the high temperatures used in solar absorption chillers.

as high as 300°F. Since conventional flat-plate collectors can seldom achieve an output temperature in excess of 200°F, the result would be reduced system efficiency and an increase in necessary collector area. This causes space and money problems.

Thanks to research being done largely in the United States and Japan, these difficulties are being slowly overcome. One American manufacturer has developed an absorption chiller with a design inlet temperature of only 195°F, and some modified models can function at as low a temperature as 160°F. The Japanese, also, have succeeded in producing a chiller with an inlet temperature of less than 170°F.

There have also been advances in collector design that make efficient operation at higher temperatures more feasible. The substitution of selective coatings for black paint on absorber plates has made double glazing unnecessary in many applications. However, for solar cooling black paint and double glazing can be teamed to increase the temperature output of a collector. The evacuated-tube collector (Fig. 9.5) can also contribute effectively. The object of these innovations is to power a solar cooling system efficiently with as little collector area as possible in order to bring costs into line. Ideally, economy will be furthered even more by allowing the same collectors that cool in summer to do the heating job as well.

Chapter 10

PASSIVE SOLAR ENERGY

Active solar systems can be adapted to many types of homes. Extensive use of passive solar energy, however, often depends on design considerations that must be made before ground is broken for a new structure. As we noted earlier, the building is the system and the system is the building. (See Fig. 10.1.)

Nevertheless, no homeowner should be without some grasp of the basics of passive solar heating and cooling. For one thing, there are

Fig. 10.1 A passive solar home in the Vermont countryside. (Courtesy Green Mountain Homes.)

frequent opportunities for taking at least partial advantage of passive solar energy even in conventional homes—opportunities that are all too often ignored or even turned into energy liabilities. Also, an appreciation of passive solar principles can lead to a more efficient use of whatever source of energy is used to create the indoor climate. Another reason that any home owner should know about passive solar energy is that there are benefits that can be derived from home additions such as solar greenhouses. Finally, an awareness of energy-conscious design can be applied to the purchase or building of a future home. The new solar houses begin to look a good deal less strange when we come to understand the sound reasoning behind their architectural design and engineering.

In a cold climate the first principle of passive home design is to allow as much solar energy as possible to enter a building and to retain as much as is practical. But there are qualifications. In the summer the same house that is able to welcome solar warmth should be capable of blocking it out; in winter the means of entry for the sun's rays should not become the means for heat escape as soon as it gets dark. The careful solar designer must therefore strike a number of balances, the first of which begins with the selection of a building site.

Windows in a passive solar home must be oriented just as the collectors are in an active solar home. A passive solar home must be situated for maximum solar gain from 9:00 A.M. to 3:00 P.M. when the sun is sufficiently high in the winter sky. This means that the major glass areas will be located along the southern exposure of the building. The east and west sides of the building will have fewer windows, and the north side the fewest of all.

The orientation not only of the windows but of the house itself is of prime concern in solar design. In *The Passive Solar Energy Book*, Edward Mazria points out that a house elongated along an east-west axis is best in all climates. Such a house presents its broadest exposure to the south for winter heat gain, while its narrower eastern and western sides offer as little surface as possible to the intense rays of the summer sun (Fig. 10.2). Especially if there is a properly-designed overhang above the south-facing windows, there is little risk of excessive heat gain through these surfaces in summer. The reason is that the high summer sun sheds most of its rays on the roof and on the eastern and western exposures of a building. Mazria goes on to suggest that, if possible, a house should be built on the north side of its lot facing south. That way, there is less chance of obstructing sunlight and more sun available for outdoor activities.

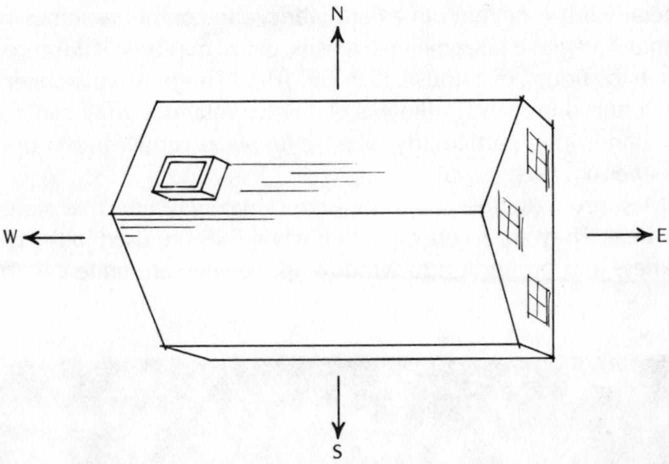

Fig. 10.2 Ideally, the narrow ends of a house should face east and west, with the greatest amount of window glass facing south.

Detailed calculation of the sun's position relative to a planned solar home at different times of the day and year can be accomplished through the use of a sun chart. This chart takes into account the constantly changing *altitude* and *azimuth* of the sun in its path through the sky. Altitude is the angle of the sun above the horizon, and azimuth is its angular deviation from true south. These coordinates are important if a builder wishes to accurately estimate heat gain, obstructions to sunlight, the optimum location of windows, and extent of overhang. For details on plotting a sun chart, see the Mazria book (listed in the bibliography at the end of this book) or consult an architect experienced in solar home design.

STORING PASSIVELY GAINED HEAT

In an active solar heating system, heat can be stored at a location remote from the point of its collection, provided, of course, that the storage facility is well insulated and that the length of the pipes or ducts that run between collectors and storage is not excessive. Heat gained directly in a passive solar home is also stored although not in an isolated tank or bin. An important feature of all true passive designs is a heat-retaining mass located directly in the path of sunlight received through windows.

This does not mean a rock bin under the sofa. (Although the sofa itself, especially if it is covered in a dark fabric, can contribute somewhat to thermal storage.) It *does* mean extensive use of masonry at the core, and even in the floors, of a house. (See Fig. 10.3.) This massive architectural treatment is one of the hallmarks of passive solar design. It can also be quite handsome, particularly when a fireplace is built into a brick or stone thermal storage wall.

Masonry, concrete, and stone are amazingly effective storers of solar heat. They are so effective that when they are used in the proper thickness and proportion to window space, they are quite capable of

Fig. 10.3 Nighttime view of the interior of the Whitney residence in south central Maine. The house, designed by Solar Design Associates of Canton, Massachusetts, relies in large part upon passive solar energy to fulfill its heating requirements.

Sunlight is welcomed into the house through the large south facing window wall. The massive masonry fireplace core and stone floor store this passive solar energy, absorbing daytime gains to help keep the house comfortably warm with outdoor temperatures that frequently get down to 20 below zero.

retaining sufficient heat to tide the occupants of a passive solar home through a cold winter night—with little or no assistance from conventional heating equipment. A single woodstove is often all that is needed for the auxiliary heating of a full-sized house, except for when the house is to be left vacant for several days or more.

In a house heated by passive solar energy, the use of auxiliaries is geared to the same circumstances that make them necessary in an actively heated solar dwelling—that is, depletion of stored heat and insufficient sunshine for direct warming of the living areas. Thermostatic controls can play the same role as in other homes in determining when assistance is necessary.

Even though a passive solar home lacks elaborate heating and cooling machinery, there are still a number of ways in which the system can be "fine-tuned" for comfort and efficiency. Like a home heated by any other means, a passive solar home can be consistently too warm or too cool if its design elements are not balanced correctly.

Overheating in a passive system can be caused by too much window space in relation to the floor area of the building or by insufficient thermal storage for the heat received. In the latter case the problem of uncomfortable heat during periods of bright sunshine will be compounded by that of rapidly fluctuating temperatures and cold evenings. The best design is that which provides a steady supply of heat.

Edward Mazria suggests that in a temperate climate there be a ratio of 0.11 to 0.25 square feet of south-facing glass to each square foot of floor space in the area to be heated. For cold climates, his ratio is 0.19–0.38 to each square foot. In addition, he recommends that the depth of the area to be heated and illuminated through the windows in a passive design should not exceed 2 to 2½ times the height of the windows (as measured from the floor). According to Mazria, temperature stability in a passive home is best assured by providing at least 4 inches of masonry or concrete as a heat-retaining mass.

If this thermal storage extends to floors as well as walls, and if the window space is properly proportioned to the area of the storage mass, uncomfortable fluctuations in temperature will not take place even if this 4-inch minimum is not exceeded. If the glass-to-storage ratio is insufficient, even substantial thickening of the masonry will not remedy the situation.

Color also has an effect. Masonry floors should be dark (without wall-to-wall carpets), while massive walls can be any color. Light-colored surfaces will reflect sunlight to darker areas. This is preferable to concentrating the sun's rays directly on the darker areas as they can

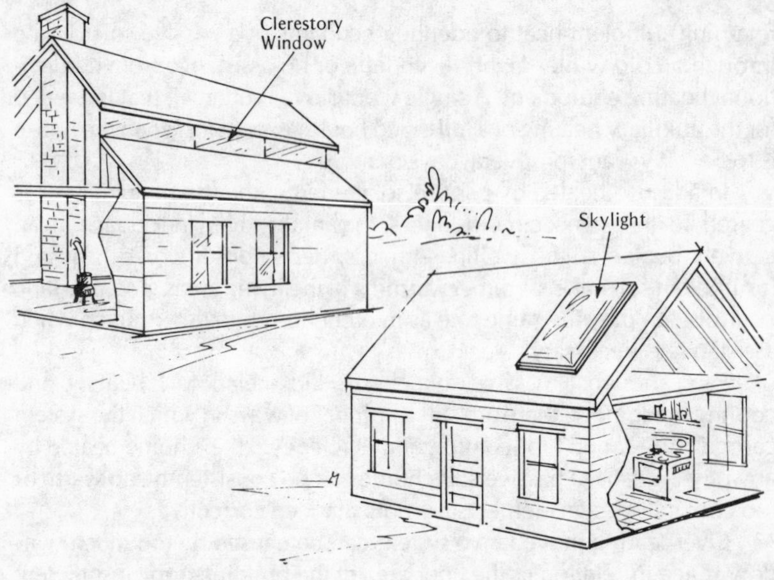

Fig. 10.4 Clerestory windows (left) and skylights (right) can provide gentle natural light as well as passive solar heat.

overheat and thus immediately give off, rather than store, the warmth they receive. When "richocheting" of solar radiation from light to dark surfaces is not feasible, translucent (light-diffusing) glazing can help accomplish the same effect and ensure even storage of warmth from sunlight.

Windows are not the only means of providing access to light and warmth from the sun in a passive solar house. Skylights and clerestories —low windows placed near the ceiling, usually at a step in the roof-line—can be effective as well as pleasing to the eye (Fig. 10.4).

Nor are masonry walls the only means of heat retention. Many of the more innovative solar houses, particularly in the American South-west, incorporate water storage into their designs. The principle is the same: sunlight entering a south-facing window warms the storage mass, which in turn releases heat slowly during nighttime and cloudy periods. The physical details of water storage can be worked out in a number of ways, ranging from the homemade to the prefabricated. One of the simplest and most successful schemes uses a bank of horizontally mounted steel drums, their outward-facing ends painted black for

Fig. 10.5 Vertical tubes, made of a fiberglass-reinforced polymer, hold water for solar heat storage. A translucent finish or black selective surface, for greater heat absorption, may be specified. (Courtesy Kalwall Corp.)

greater solar absorption. Or, it is possible to purchase columnlike steel or fiberglass tubing—inverted highway culvert has been used effectively—and install it on a stable base in the path of winter sunlight (Fig. 10.5). Many of the commercially manufactured containers already will have a protective lining; makeshift storage vessels such as steel drums should be protected from corrosion by the addition of a stabilizer to the water that they hold.

The chief advantage of water as a passive storage medium is its ability to retain more heat in a smaller volume. It will also warm faster and give off heat more quickly than masonry or concrete. Its principal drawbacks are the unconventional appearance of the necessary containers, and the need for a solid foundation below any sizeable amount of water. Masonry heat storage, on the other hand, is generally an integral part of the building mass itself and as such presents no strain on floors or foundations in a properly designed building.

PASSIVE HEATING AND INTERIOR LAYOUT

Sound solar architecture also takes into consideration the arrangement of living and working spaces inside a house. It stands to reason that the areas in which warmth and light are most important should be grouped around the southern exposure where sunshine is most abundant (Fig. 10.6). The northern side of the building can be reserved for occasional bedrooms, utility rooms, and storage.

In many passive homes the idea of "rooms" has been refined somewhat, since the even circulation of heat throughout the building is

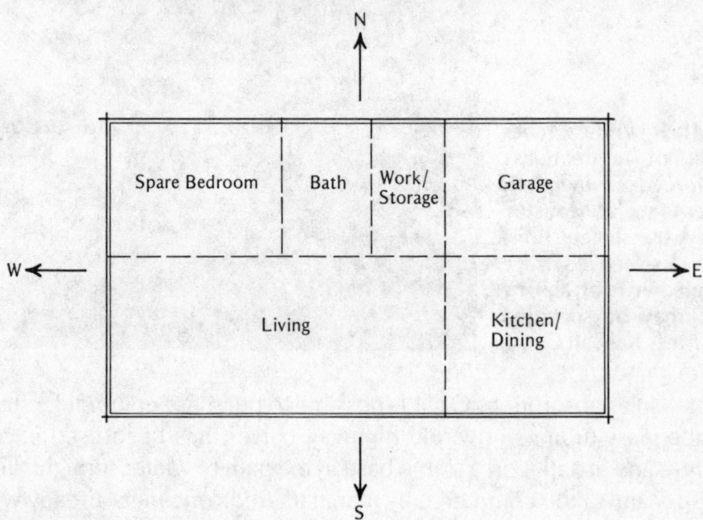

Fig. 10.6 In a passive solar house, rooms used most frequently should be grouped near warmer southern exposure.

important and will not, in most cases, be facilitated by localized radiators or air ducts. A passive home need not resemble an open barn, however. As more and more architects and engineers begin to tackle the challenge of designing homes that work with climate rather than against it, sophisticated and visually exciting buildings, respectful of traditional ideas of privacy and separation of domestic functions, are appearing throughout North America.

THE TROMBE WALL: A PASSIVE DEVICE FOR INDIRECT SOLAR GAIN

The type of passive solar heating that we have been discussing so far is based on the principle of *direct* solar gain, that is, solar energy that is stored and released at the points where it is initially received. Without relying on active machinery, it is still possible to derive warmth from sunlight at other locations in the home. There are several ways to accomplish this. In a sense, the water storage units mentioned earlier provide a means of indirect gain since solar heat strikes one side of the units and is radiated into the room from the other. One of the most famous and successful of the indirect gain applications is the *Trombe wall*, named for Dr. Felix Trombe, a French solar pioneer.

Trombe walls operate in much the same way as flat-plate solar collectors, but they differ from collectors in that the heat they absorb is distributed to where it is needed without mechanical assistance. In addition to their usefulness in new passive homes, Trombe walls also present an appealing opportunity for indirect heat gain in south-facing additions to existing buildings.

A Trombe wall is not one wall but two. Its outer surface is glass; double glazing is often used to improve heat retention. Although the overall surface of this window-wall should be as transparent as possible, it is acceptable to install the glass in partitioned sections if the area to be covered is too large for uninterrupted large panes to be practical.

So far what we have is a picture window. Now comes the inner wall that enables the sunlight and glass to do their work. This partition is located parallel to and several inches behind the glass. The partition is constructed of stone, masonry, or concrete—the same materials used for thermal storage in full-scale passive home designs. The surface of the wall facing the glass is painted flat black, just like the absorber plate in a solar collector. The overall thickness of the wall is generally between 4 and 16 inches. Its surface may be interrupted by fixed, glazed windows although any significant deviation from the wall's thickness and opacity will partially defeat its effectiveness. Dampered vents are located at the top and bottom of the wall.

The Trombe wall supplies solar heat to a room both by convection and radiation. Remember the convection principle put to work when currents of air rise through open skylights or vented air-type collectors, causing cool drafts to circulate through the rooms below? The Trombe wall works on the same idea although its main function is to warm rather than cool a room. (See Fig. 10.7.)

The Trombe wall works as follows. When sunlight falls upon the outer, glass surface of the wall, it heats the air sandwiched between the masonry and the glass. The greenhouse effect assures the trapping of this heat. As this air grows warmer, it gains in buoyancy and rises through the open vents near the top of the inner wall. It is constantly replaced by the denser, colder air that lies near the floor of the room; this air enters the vents at the bottom of the wall and the process is continued. There is a constant exchange of warm air for cold, just as in a room served by the outlet and return ducts of a forced-air furnace.

The dampers in the wall vents are a provision against a "backfire" of the system at night or during cold, cloudy periods. If the vents were always left open, warm room air would be brought into contact with the cold glass and would come back as uncomfortable drafts.

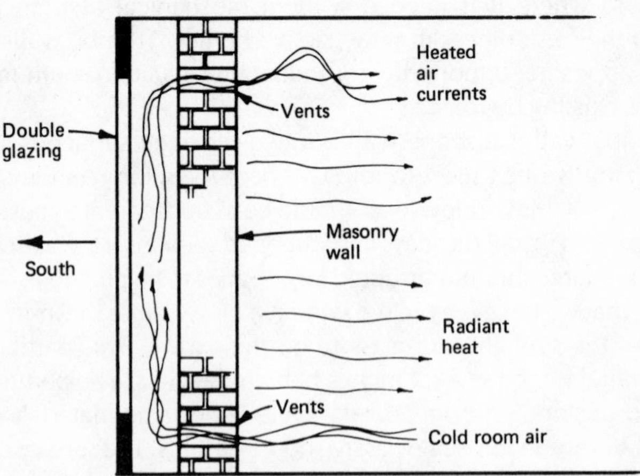

Fig. 10.7 The Trombe wall heats via convection and radiation. Vents can be closed to prevent nighttime "Backfire."

Although the vents are dampered at sunset, the heating function of the wall continues. This is the time of day when radiation takes over from convection as the means by which the Trombe wall heats the adjacent room. Throughout the time when the sun was shining, the black-painted surface of the interior wall was absorbing solar heat, reaching temperatures as high as 150°F. Now it will reradiate this heat through its opposite surface and into the room—in the same way that the water storage devices we looked at earlier do. It is this two-way heating ability of the Trombe wall that makes it a particularly interesting variation on basic passive solar design.

By installing a transomlike vent near the top of the glass outer wall in a Trombe installation, it is possible to add yet another function—summer cooling (Fig. 10.8). Once again, a planned convection current is used. The method is to open windows on the opposite, north-facing side of the room, and to close the upper vents in the masonry portion of the Trombe wall. The lower vent, along with the vent at the top of the glass, remains open. As in winter the sun warms and increases the buoyancy of air traveling between the masonry and the glass. Only this time, the heated air leaves the building rather than cycling back into the room. This convection draft is fed by continuous intake from the north-facing windows, with the result being a welcome change of air and lowered temperatures in the room.

CONSERVING HEAT IN PASSIVE SOLAR HOMES

Earlier we observed that the need to admit as much heat as possible into a passive solar home is accompanied by the need to allow as little of it as

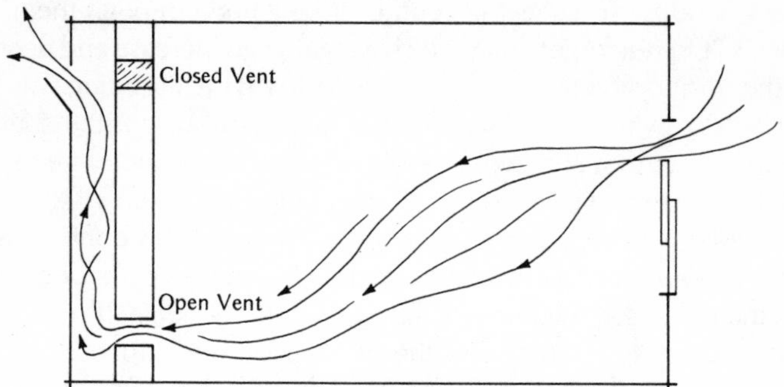

Fig. 10.8 A vent in the window of a Trombe wall can make the fixture capable of cooling as well as heating. Heat-induced drafts (convection) are the secret.

possible to escape on cold winter evenings. The question of warm weather comfort is just as important, especially in climates where air conditioning represents an expensive and perpetual drain on energy resources. Many of the measures taken to conserve heat in a passive home will work to keep the indoor environment pleasant in summer as well. Cooling can also be accomplished by means of convection, as we have already seen. In certain climates, it is also possible to manage a complete reversal of solar collection and heat storage methods by capturing coolness at night and using it during the day.

Extensive glass surfaces are one of the critical features of passive solar design. Without them sufficient heat gain would be impossible, and thermal storage masses could not be made to function. The heat *conducting* abilities of glass are well known; we have all seen the infrared photographs that reveal the effectiveness of home insulation and observed that the greatest drain of heat takes place at the windows. Glass, in the thickness used for windows, has the lowest R value of any of the materials that make up a home's exterior surface. A square foot of glass will allow twenty times as much heat to be conducted through its surface as an entire insulated wall when the temperature is 30°F outside and 68°F indoors. How does one keep the glass in a passive solar home from becoming as much of a liability as an asset, from becoming, in effect, a revolving door for solar heat?

Correct window placement is one answer. The reason that the eastern and western exposures of a passive solar house have less window surface than the southern exposure, and that the northern exposure has the least of all, is not only that the opportunity for solar gain is greatest at the south side, but that heat loss is also a factor. The simple fact is that much more heat will escape from the northern, eastern, and western window surfaces than can ever be gained through them. (See Fig. 10.9.) Do not forget that while solar gain can increase and decrease with the positioning of a window, heat loss will be just as great at night regardless of which way the window faces. For all but the southern exposure (and, to a somewhat lesser degree, the southeast and southwest), the result will be a net drain rather than a net gain.

Another way to conserve absorbed heat is to employ double glazing wherever possible. The insulating secret of a double pane of glass lies not in the increased thickness of the material itself, but in the creation of a pocket of dead air between the two transparent surfaces. Air thus trapped is an excellent insulator; anyone who has ever poured hot coffee from a thermos bottle can attest to that. (However, air space in walls cannot match the insulating ability of the solid materials used for

Fig. 10.9 Note window layout in this passive solar home. Large windows (actually sliding glass doors) face south, with overhang sufficient to block summer sun. Eastern exposure (right side of photo), however, has very little window area. (Courtesy Green Mountain Homes.)

the walls themselves. The air space is invariably set in motion by drafts that can then convect heat away from the house. The effectiveness of the standard home's insulating materials is in fact based upon their being able to trap and *hold still* pockets of air, such as the foam bubbles or the tiny spaces between spun glass fibers do.)

In very cold climates even the south-facing windows in a passive house can benefit from double glazing, although the interference of an extra pane of glass can result in somewhat reduced solar gain. An architect or housing engineer experienced in passive solar design in your area should be able to evaluate the overall benefit or detriment to the system that this modification would pose. For windows on all other sides of the house, however, double glazing is strongly recommended. Many passive designers even go so far as to specify triple glazing on the north side, if there are any windows there at all. The extra expense will be nominal since the glass surfaces on all but the south side are kept to a minimum in the first place. Recessing the windows can also help cut heat losses (Fig. 10.10).

Another means of keeping heat indoors is to provide some form of movable insulation at the windows, particularly those in vulnerable

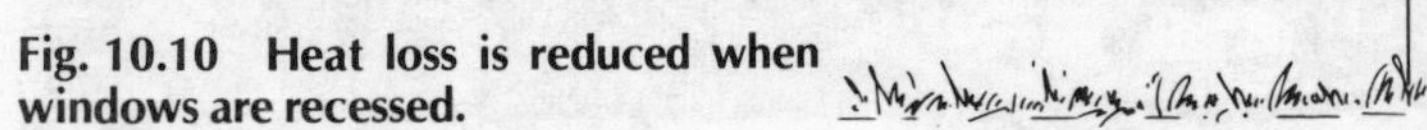

Fig. 10.10 **Heat loss is reduced when windows are recessed.**

locations. there are now a great many products designed for this purpose on the market ranging from quilted shades, to snug fitting shutters (Fig. 10.11), to drapes lined with a heat-reflecting silvery material similar to the "space blankets" used for outdoor winter emer-

Fig. 10.11 Fabric-covered panel at right of photo is an insulating shutter, designed to prevent nighttime escape of heat gained during day through south-facing window. (Courtesy Green Mountain Homes.)

gencies. Needless to say, the usefulness of these window insulators extends to conventional as well as passive solar homes, especially when drafts, as well as radiation, are a source of heat loss.

Building Sites and Heat Conservation

Protection of windows is only part of the program of heat conservation in a passive solar house. The physical aspects of the building site also play an important role. Since one of the main threats to winter comfort in cold climates is the north wind, it makes sense to show not only as little window area but also as little surface of any sort to the north. This is why passive solar homes, where feasible, are built into south-facing hillsides, or are protected by a mound of earth (called a *berm*) buttressed against their north sides. Berm houses are nothing new; they were used by prairie settlers who had no other protection from scouring winter winds. With attractive landscaping and the right arrangement of interior spaces, a berm house need not be reminiscent of a tornado shelter. (See Fig. 10.12.)

Wind can also be thwarted by being forced over or around a house. One of the advantages of the saltbox design (Fig. 10.13) is that if the longer roof surface at the back of the house can be faced to the north, direct contact between wind and walls will be reduced. Plantings of evergreens in the path of a prevailing north wind can also lessen its heat-robbing effect.

Every potential building site has what is called a "microclimate." Although related to regional weather patterns, the conditions that make up a site's microclimate are largely created by immediate factors such as the lay of the land (Fig. 10.14), the presence of bodies of water, and the degree to which the surrounding area has been built up. Anyone plan-

Fig. 10.12 An earth berm can provide both insulation and wind protection. If the design is handled properly, the berm house will appear to be in harmony with the surrounding landscape.

Fig. 10.13 Long, sloping roof of saltbox design can effectively shield house from north winds. (Courtesy Green Mountain Homes.)

Fig. 10.14 Wooded ridge protects this house from cold north and northeasterly winds. (Courtesy Green Mountain Homes.)

ning to build a house—using passive solar energy or not—would do well to examine the microclimates of the construction sites being considered.

It is unwise, for instance, to build in a spot lying at the end of a naturally formed wind channel. Wind speeds will be consistently higher there than at other nearby locations. Unprotected hilltops are also windy, but that does not mean that the bottom of a hollow would be a better choice. Cold air settles in low lying places, and they are the last to warm up when the weather changes. Large bodies of water can help moderate a climate both in summer and winter since the water constitutes thermal mass of a sort. If a site's microclimate includes a north wind blowing off a frozen lake during the coldest months of the year, the prospect of offshore breezes in summer may not be enough to justify the location, at least if passive heating and energy conservation are among a prospective builder's goals.

It is often forgotten that part of a building's passively acquired heat originates indoors and not from the rays of the sun. Where does it come from? Look no further than your own body, which generates approximately 400 Btu of excess heat each hour. The superior insulation of a good passive home can help contain this free heat, along with the not inconsiderable amounts put out by household appliances (Fig. 10.15). All of these Btu add up—so much so that they are taken into consideration with increasing frequency when the heat loads of new commercial buildings are calculated by forward-thinking architects.

Fig. 10.15 Not all of the heat in a house comes from a furnace, or the sun. Insulation helps conserve waste heat from people and appliances.

PASSIVE COOLING

We have already observed examples of how the solar-generated convection process can help cool a home through the use of Trombe walls and vented air-type collectors. This principle of ventilation should be put to work whenever possible in new home design, as well as in the use of conventional features in older homes. Attic vents and open windows on upper as well as lower stories can lower indoor temperatures considerably. Also, do not forget the wind patterns in your particular microclimate. Cooling breezes can be channeled effectively by careful fencing and planting of shrubs.

Ventilation patterns are only one of the factors involved in passive cooling. Another, of course, is shade. Shade is one reason why designers of solar homes are so concerned not only with orientation but with the height of the sun in the summer sky. If south-facing windows are given the proper amount of overhang, rays of sunshine unobstructed in winter will be blocked effectively come June, July, and August. Other forms of shading—such as hardwood trees—are also important.

Trees, in fact, contribute more than just shade to the cooling of a site. Their solar-powered evaporation and convection processes also help. The secret is in the leaves. A healthy tree is always drawing water from the soil, and its leaves are the recipients of this moisture. Water is steadily evaporated from the surface of the leaves by the energy of the sun. As a result of the process of absorption and evaporation of water, heat is drawn from the surrounding area and a gentle, upward draft of air is created. Thus the sun, with the help of trees (and all green growing things), becomes not only the source of heat, but also the means of relief from uncomfortably warm summer weather.

Insulation, which is so necessary for conserving stored solar heat in wintertime, is also a big help in summer. Think of insulation not simply as something that keeps heat in, but as something that *blocks* heat whatever direction it comes from. In the winter a great deal of heat can be lost through an uninsulated roof. This being the case, imagine how much unwanted heat is liable to be *gained* through such a poorly protected surface when the sun's path is directly overhead during summer.

The protective drapes, shades, and shutters used in winter to hold heat after nightfall are also useful for keeping indoor temperatures down, especially in a house that, although it might have substantial window space, was not designed with the correct amount of shading overhang and thus must bear the full brunt of summer sunshine. (See Fig. 10.16.)

Fig. 10.16 "Solarcool"™ windows admit warmth in winter, yet block excessive summer radiation. (Courtesy PPG Industries.)

The subject of blocking off sunlight from windows brings us to another method of passive cooling, one which is especially effective in areas experiencing hot days and cool, dry nights. (Much of the American West fits this description.) The idea is to shutter windows during the day and to remove the coverings at night. As is true in passive solar heating, the best results are achieved when the windows work together with a nearby thermal mass, but the scheme is worth trying even in a conventional home if the climate is favorable.

All passive heating and cooling techniques—indeed, *all* climate-control systems including oil furnaces and electric air conditioners—operate on the principle that heat seeks whatever cooler objects or environments are nearby. If sunlight is blocked out, the thermal mass is prevented from accumulating solar heat during the day and instead stores up warmth drawn from indoors. At night, when the shutters are opened, this heat is given off into the cooler outdoor environment. By morning the mass is "drained" of heat and ready once again to cool the living area by drawing warmth from it.

Among the most successful working examples of this principle have been the houses that use water stored in windowside containers as thermal mass. (See description earlier in this chapter.) Imaginative track and pulley systems have been devised for alternately exposing and protecting the storage media; in some instances, these surfaces could be described as movable walls.

It is not at the windows or walls but on the roof that one of the most innovative systems of heat storage and release has been applied. Often referred to as "roof ponds," these installations consist of water-filled polyvinyl chloride (PVC) bags, arranged over the surface of specially designed flat roofs. Sliding insulated panels (motor-driven in the more sophisticated versions) complete the picture. (See Fig. 10.17.) The prin-

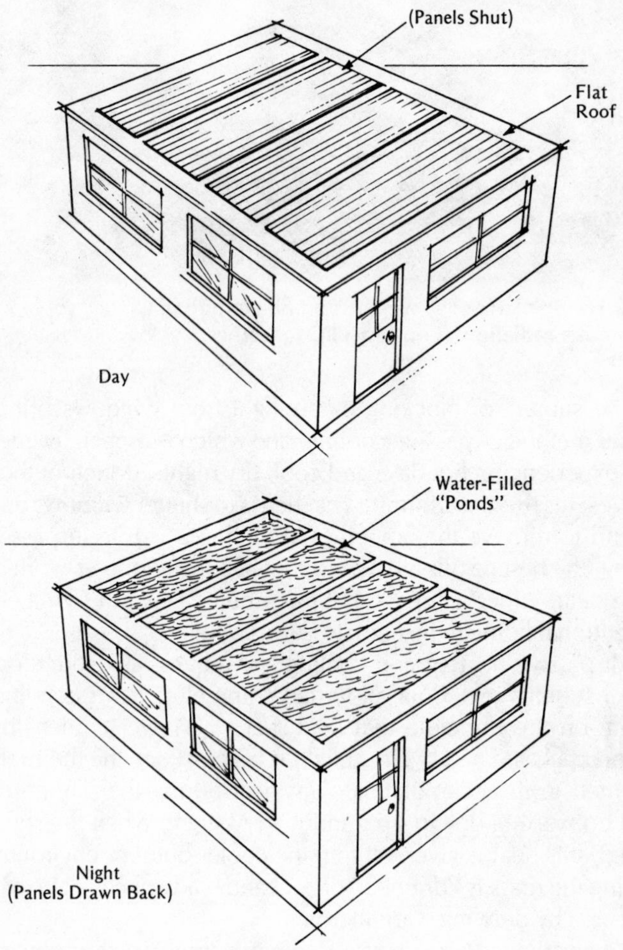

Fig. 10.17 PVC "ponds" on flat roof absorb heat from house during day; when cover panels are drawn back, heat dissipates into cool night sky.

ciple is the same: the water in the bags absorbs heat from the house during the day while the panels are in place above them; at night, with the panels drawn back, this heat is radiated into the night sky. There is no reason why the process cannot work in reverse for heating in winter, and in fact roof pond homes built in mild climates have given quite excellent results in all seasons. However, the need for provision against freezing (i.e., a second roof, with double-glazed skylights) makes the pond a much more viable choice in climates in which air conditioning is a greater concern than heating.

SOLAR GREENHOUSES

Of all the passive solar applications, the one exciting the most public interest in virtually all climates is the solar greenhouse (Fig. 10.18). The reason is twofold: greenhouses can be built onto many types of houses regardless of whether or not other passive or active features are in place,

Fig. 10.18 This solar greenhouse, built as an integral part of a passive solar home in Maine, helps heat an adjacent workshop. (Courtesy Solar Design Associates.)

and the idea of year-round indoor gardening carries even more appeal than that of saving money on energy.

A good solar greenhouse can do more than simply "break even" in terms of energy; it can actually help supply heat to the house itself. All this is possible through efficient use of the basic principles of passive heating: thermal storage, insulation, and, of course, the greenhouse effect.

A solar greenhouse is essentially a lean-to structure installed against the south side of a house. (Free-standing solar greenhouses can be built but their north sides must be vertical, opaque, and heavily insulated.) Because the wall of the house becomes the greenhouse's north wall, there is no danger of heat drain from that surface; similarly, the eastern and western exposures are heavily insulated, incorporating little or no glass area. All of the glazing, then, faces south, and should consist ideally of double panes. Despite the prevalence of all-glass construction in conventional greenhouses, the solar gain through the glazing of the south-facing wall and sloping roof of a well-designed solar greenhouse is more than sufficient for a great many popular ornamental and food plants. In very cold climates satisfactory results are even achieved with an elimination of all glazing from the roof surface.

Double-glazing alone is not sufficient to guard the greenhouse from nighttime temperature drops. For this reason a system of removable insulating panels, or shutters, operable on either the inside or outside of the structure, is essential. An example of the difference that insulating shutters makes is illustrated by a Maine greenhouse having a total of 404 square feet of glazing and a heat gain of 498,700 Btu per day. Before the installation of shutters, heat loss was 514,000 Btu per day, putting the structure over 15,000 Btu in the red. After shutters were added, heat loss dropped to just under 300,000 Btu per day. In addition, the shutters installed on this particular greenhouse consisted of exterior-mounted white panels that had when open a reflective ability capable of adding another 100,000 Btu to the base heat gain. (Snow, by the way, is also an excellent reflector of sunlight and should not be shoveled away from the vicinity of the greenhouse.)

Any number of shutter materials and designs have been tried. One popular solution is to sandwich 2 inches of styrofoam beadboard between thermoply material in a frame made of 3/4 × 2 inch strips. The aluminum surface of the thermoply sheet faces up on the outer face of the panel and down on the inside. For outdoor shutters an outer rim of extruded aluminum or steel, or of aluminum flashing material, can be used along with butylene caulking to weatherproof the framing and the edges of the thermoply.

Indoor panels will not need this protection. The shutter panels can be hinged at their centers, installed on tracks, and opened butterfly fashion, or hinged only at their ends and lifted in and out of place in one piece. The latter choice will provide more reflective area for outdoor panels. The long poles used to open and close tall windows are handy tools for raising and lowering greenhouse shutter panels; to use them, simply fasten a metal loop to the center of each panel. (See Fig. 10.19.)

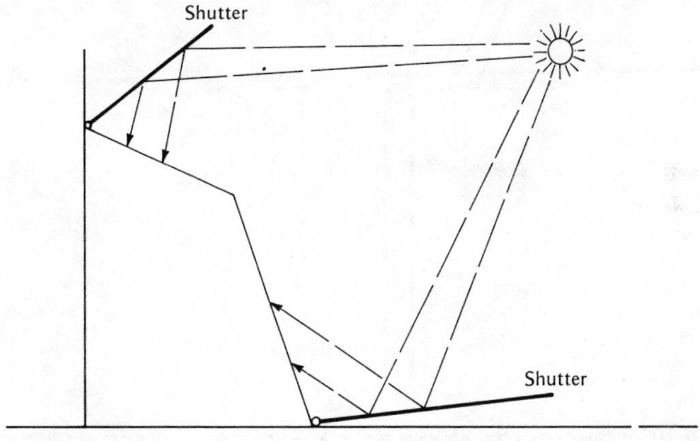

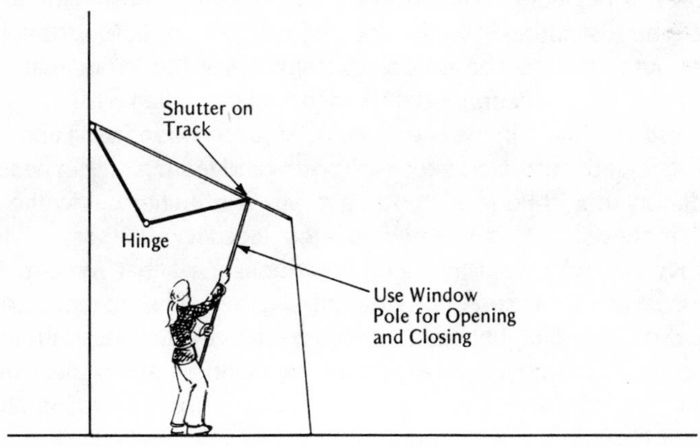

Fig. 10.19 Two possible shutter treatments for a solar greenhouse. At top, outdoor shutters designed to reflect sunlight when open. At bottom, indoor shutters, hinged to fold when opened.

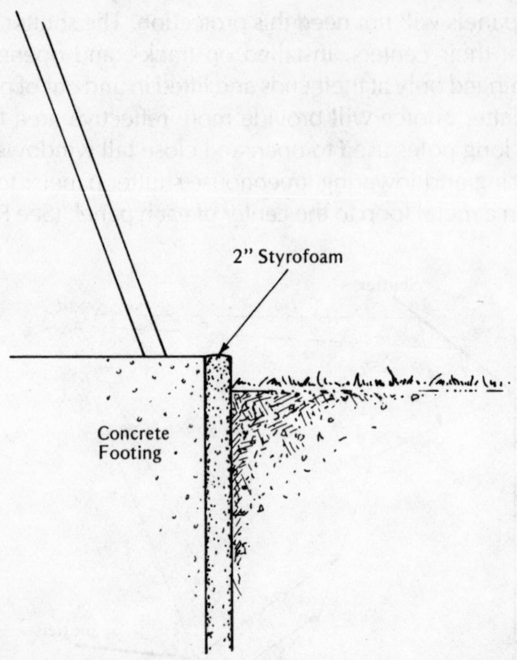

Fig. 10.20 Styrofoam panels can serve as insulation for concrete footings in solar greenhouse.

Do not neglect insulation in the unglazed portions of the greenhouse. The east and west walls, along with the footing below the glazing on the south side, must be as heat-resistant as possible. Wooden framing should be built to accommodate 6 inches of insulation; still more may be necessary if the climate is very cold. As for the foundation and floor, concrete can be insulated effectively with rigid foam panels. The entire foundation should be insulated to a depth of 6 inches below the frost line; 2 inches of styrofoam will do the job. (See Fig. 10.20.)

Given a tight, well-insulated greenhouse, all that remains is to provide it with some sort of thermal storage that will keep temperatures stable during cold nights. Because of the relative quickness with which it absorbs heat, and because of the compactness and variety of the containers available for it, water is often the storage material of choice for small home solar greenhouses.

Black-painted metal drums are acceptable containers (again, add anticorrosive stabilizers if water is to come in contact with metal), as are plastic jugs or carboys. The size of the individual containers is not crucial, although some solar greenhouse designers point out that above a certain capacity (for instance, with a 55-gallon drum) the surface-to-volume ratio becomes insufficient. Also, temperatures will stratify within a large container more readily than in a small one. Air circulation is a factor as well; more air will make contact with heated surfaces if the storage mass consists of a battery of smaller containers stacked so as to allow circulation.

Masonry and rock bins are less frequently used for heat storage in small solar greenhouses because of the volume of material required. However, do not overlook the thermal retention properties of a gravel or concrete floor. To make sure that heat stored in this surface radiates upwards into the greennhouse, rather than downwards into the ground, insulate with styrofoam *below* the foundation. Moisture-proofing can be accomplished with the use of a 24-mil polyethylene sheet.

Where do you locate water storage? One answer is to arrange the drums or battery of small containers right near the glazing in the direct path of sunlight; another, more commonly accepted, is to situate the storage facility along the wall shared by the house and greenhouse. That way heat will be more evenly distributed to both structures, especially if the proper ventilation is provided. In a well designed solar greenhouse the heat-retaining mass of water containers need not be obtrusive; they can even form the base for a work table or plant bench. Keep in mind that the path of sunlight to the storage mass should not be impeded and that a light-colored floor will reflect heat toward the dark storage vessels. (See Fig. 10.21.)

Although electric fans can be used to help distribute stored heat, both within the greenhouse and into the home, natural convection is often all that is required to assure this process. Air exchange between the main building and the addition is desirable both for transferring stored solar warmth into the home, and for backup heating of the greenhouse during prolonged periods of bad weather. Therefore, the greenhouse should be built so that at least a door, and perhaps a window as well, forms a part of the wall that it shares with the house.

Ideally, there might even be vents in the wall near floor level. These openings would allow cold air to exit the house and rise through the thermal storage mass; heated, these currents would reenter the house at window level or through other vents placed higher in the wall. What you would have, in effect, would be a giant Trombe wall that you could garden in. The greenhouse would also assume a Trombelike function in the summer, as warm house air was exhausted through vents near the top of its glazed surface.

Solar greenhouses, then, represent an exciting reversal of the tradeoff usually made by homeowners who wish to grow plants under

Fig. 10.21 In this large solar greenhouse, 55-gallon drums are acceptable for heat storage. Note trellis against face of drums. (Courtesy Solar Sustenance Team, Route 1, Box 107AA, Santa Fe, NM 87501.)

glass in all seasons. Rather than demand extra energy, they can pay their own way with a nice amount of change left over.

HYBRID SYSTEMS AND HYBRID THINKING

For purposes of explanation, it is often convenient to separate "active" and "passive" solar applications, as we have done here, into two distinct categories. They are, however, far from incompatible. Both are based on the same principles of heat exchange; both make minimal demands on the environment; both offer wonderful opportunities for conservation of energy resources as well as for saving money.

A user of active solar equipment must invariably come to a greater understanding of the ideas behind passive heating and cooling; his or

Fig. 10.22 A hybrid solar home. Despite a severe northern New England climate, active and passive solar features supply nearly 100 percent of the heat and hot water for this house. A wood stove and fireplace provide all the assistance needed. (Courtesy Solar Design Associates.

her collectors and storage system function by way of absorbing, retaining, and releasing heat. Can such a person long neglect such things as insulation, window protection, exposure to winter sunlight, and shading and ventilation in summer? Similarly, the owner of a passive home cannot think of himself or herself as being above technology. A great deal of sophisticated calculation and slide rule gymnastics have gone into the study of thermodynamics for the design of passive systems. Is an active collector array for, say, domestic hot water or supplementary space heat so out of keeping with this type of house?

The answer, of course, is no. Houses which feature applications of both active and passive solar technology are called hybrid houses (Fig. 10.22); we might pose the idea of "hybrid thinking" as well. This is the type of thinking that integrates ideas, that makes leaps between one set of facts and another in pursuit of the common line of sense and efficiency that runs through them. In energy, as nowhere else, is this thinking necessary, and the design of comfortable living spaces is the point at which it touches us all.

Appendix A

CALCULATING HEAT LOAD

Every building has a "heat load." This is the amount of heat that must be generated—or, in a solar home, released from storage—in order to equal the amount lost through its surfaces. If you remember that heat constantly travels away from warmer objects toward colder ones, you will understand why keeping a house comfortable consists of striking a balance between heat gain and heat loss.

Except in all-electric homes where heating requirements are often calculated in terms of kilowatt-hours, heat load is generally represented by the amount of British thermal units (Btu) lost per hour. One Btu is equivalent to the amount of heat energy required to raise the temperature of 1 pint (1 pound) of water by 1°F. The hourly basis is used because that is how the Btu output of heat-producing equipment is rated. For example, if a furnace is rated at 90,000 Btu, that will be its output over one hour.

In order to figure the heat load of a building it is necessary to take into account certain data about the building itself and the climate in which it is located. Since heat *loss* is the critical factor, the heat-resisting abilities of all surfaces facing the outdoors must be known. Both the type of material and its thickness are important.

Heat resistance is expressed in R value. Most exposed surfaces are made up of several different materials each with its own R value; these are totaled for each surface, and the surfaces are then measured separately. (If the basement ceiling is not insulated, the R value of the foundation walls must also be measured. The same is true of the roof if there is no insulation in the attic floor. Otherwise, the basement ceiling/first floor and the top story ceiling/attic floor are considered as exterior surfaces.)

The total area (in square feet) of each separate surface is divided by its composite R value. The quotient is then multiplied by the *temperature difference* for the geographic location of the house. The temperature difference is figured by subtracting the lowest anticipated outdoor temperature (called the *design temperature*) from the temperature to be maintained inside the house.

When the multiples for each surface are added, the total is the house's heat load—the amount of heat lost hourly through all outside surfaces, and the amount that must be made up for by the solar and/or conventional equipment used to heat the house.

$$\frac{\text{Surface Area}}{\text{R Value}} \times \text{Temperature Difference} = \text{Heat Load}$$

If you know exactly what your floors, walls, and ceilings (or roof and foundation, if necessary) are made of, along with the R value of each material, you can come up with a fair estimate of your heat load. The only other requirements are a measuring tape and a call to the Weather Service to find out what the design temperature is for your area. A heating contractor or state extension service housing specialist can usually give assistance if you are unsure about R values.

Appendix B

SOLAR MANUFACTURERS

American Solar King Corporation
6801 New McGregor Highway
Waco, TX 76710
Evacuated tube collectors; liquid flat-plate collectors; heat pumps.

Bio-Energy Systems, Inc.
P.O. Box 489
Mountaindale Road
Spring Glen, NY 12483
SolaRoll(TM) system

Daystar Corporation
90 Cambridge Street
Burlington, MA 01803
Liquid flat-plate collectors; space heating and domestic hot water systems.

Fafco, Inc.
235 Constitution Drive
Menlo Park, CA 94025
Pool heating systems.

Green Mountain Homes, Inc.
Waterman Road
Royalton, VT 05068
Passive solar homes—architects, engineers, builders.

Grumman Energy Systems, Inc.
4175 Veterans Memorial Highway
Ronkonkoma, NY 11779

Liquid flat-plate collectors; space heating, domestic hot water and pool systems.

Kalwall Corporation
Solar Component Division
88 Pine Street
Manchester, NH 03103

Air flat-plate collectors; space heating and domestic hot water systems.

Lennox Industries
P.O. Box 1319
Columbus, OH 43216

Liquid flat-plate collectors; domestic hot water systems.

Libbey-Owens-Ford Co.
1701 E. Broadway
Toledo, OH 43605

Liquid flat-plate collectors.

Löf Brothers Solar Appliances
1615 17th Street
Denver, CO 80202

Solar pool covers.

Northrup, Inc.
302 Nichols Drive
Hutchins, TX 75141

Liquid flat-plate and concentrating collectors; space heating and domestic hot water systems.

PPG Industries, Inc.
One Gateway Center
Pittsburgh, PA 15222

Liquid flat-plate collectors; domestic hot water systems.

Revere Solar and Architectural Products, Inc.
P.O. Box 151
Rome, NY 13440

Liquid flat-plate collectors; domestic hot water systems.

Solar Design Associates
271 Washington Street
Canton, MA 02021
Active and passive solar homes—architects, engineers, builders.

Solar Energy Research Corp.
701B South Main Street
Longmont, CO 80501
Liquid and air flat-plate collectors; space and pool heating; domestic hot water systems.

Solar Industries Incorporated
Monmouth Airport Industrial Park
Farmingdale, NJ 07727
Pool heating systems; liquid flat-plate collectors.

Solaron Corporation
300 Galleria Tower
720 Colorado Boulevard
Denver, CO 80222
Air flat-plate collectors; space heating and domestic hot water systems.

Appendix C

MEAN PERCENTAGE OF POSSIBLE SUNSHINE FOR SELECTED LOCATIONS

State and Station	Years	Jan.	Feb.	Mar.	Apr.	May	June	July	Aug.	Sept.	Oct.	Nov.	Dec.	Annual
Ala. Birmingham	56	43	49	56	63	66	67	62	65	66	67	58	44	59
Montgomery	49	51	53	61	69	73	72	66	69	69	71	64	48	64
Alaska Anchorage	19	39	46	56	58	50	51	45	39	35	32	33	29	45
Fairbanks	20	34	50	61	68	55	53	45	35	31	28	38	29	44
Juneau	14	30	32	39	37	34	35	28	30	25	18	21	18	30
Nome	29	44	46	48	53	51	48	32	26	34	35	36	30	41
Ariz. Phoenix	64	76	79	83	88	93	94	84	84	89	88	84	77	85
Yuma	52	83	87	91	94	97	98	92	91	93	93	90	83	91
Ark. Little Rock	66	44	53	57	62	67	72	71	73	71	74	58	47	62
Calif. Eureka	49	40	44	50	53	54	56	51	46	52	48	42	39	49
Fresno	55	46	63	72	83	89	94	97	97	93	87	73	47	78
Los Angeles	63	70	69	70	67	68	69	80	81	80	76	79	72	73
Red Bluff	39	50	60	65	75	79	86	95	94	89	77	64	50	75
Sacramento	48	44	57	67	76	82	90	96	95	92	82	65	44	77
San Diego	68	68	67	68	66	60	60	67	70	70	70	76	71	68
San Francisco	64	53	57	63	69	70	75	68	63	70	70	62	54	66
Colo. Denver	64	67	67	65	63	61	69	68	68	71	71	67	65	67
Grand Junction	57	58	62	64	67	71	79	76	72	77	74	67	58	69
Conn. Hartford	48	46	55	56	54	57	60	62	60	57	55	46	46	56
D.C. Washington	66	46	53	56	57	61	64	64	62	62	61	54	47	58
Fla. Apalachicola	26	59	62	62	71	77	70	64	63	62	74	66	53	65
Jacksonville	60	58	59	66	71	71	63	62	63	58	58	61	53	62
Key West	45	68	75	78	78	76	70	69	71	65	65	69	66	71
Miami Beach	48	66	72	73	73	68	62	65	67	62	62	65	65	67
Tampa	63	63	67	71	74	75	66	61	64	64	67	67	61	68
Ga. Atlanta	65	48	53	57	65	68	68	62	63	65	67	60	47	60

Mean Percentage of Possible Sunshine for Selected Locations *(Cont.)*

State and Station	Years	Jan.	Feb.	Mar.	Apr.	May	June	July	Aug.	Sept.	Oct.	Nov.	Dec.	Annual
Hawaii Hilo	9	48	42	41	34	31	41	44	38	42	41	34	36	39
Honolulu	53	62	64	60	62	64	66	67	70	70	68	63	60	65
Lihue	9	48	48	48	46	51	60	58	59	67	58	51	49	54
Idaho Boise	20	40	48	59	67	68	75	89	86	81	66	46	37	66
Pocatello	21	37	47	58	64	66	72	82	81	78	66	48	36	64
Ill. Cairo	30	46	53	59	65	71	77	82	79	75	73	56	46	65
Chicago	66	44	49	53	56	63	69	73	70	65	61	47	41	59
Springfield	59	47	51	54	58	64	69	76	72	73	64	53	45	60
Ind. Evansville	48	42	49	55	61	67	73	78	76	73	67	52	42	64
Ft. Wayne	48	38	44	51	55	62	69	74	69	64	58	41	38	57
Indianapolis	63	41	47	49	55	62	68	74	70	68	64	48	39	59
Iowa Des Moines	66	56	56	56	59	62	66	75	70	64	64	53	48	62
Dubuque	54	48	52	52	58	60	63	73	67	61	55	44	40	57
Sioux City	52	55	58	58	59	63	67	75	72	67	65	53	50	63
Kans. Concordia	52	60	60	62	63	65	73	79	76	72	70	64	58	67
Dodge City	70	67	66	68	68	68	74	78	78	76	75	70	67	71
Wichita	46	61	63	64	64	66	73	80	77	73	69	67	59	69
Ky. Louisville	59	41	47	52	57	64	68	72	69	68	64	51	39	59
La. New Orleans	69	49	50	57	63	66	64	58	60	64	70	60	46	59
Shreveport	18	48	54	58	60	69	78	79	80	79	77	65	60	69
Maine Eastport	58	45	51	52	52	51	53	55	57	54	50	37	40	50
Mass. Boston	67	47	56	57	56	59	62	64	63	61	58	48	48	57
Mich. Alpena	45	29	43	52	56	59	64	70	64	52	44	24	22	51
Detroit	69	34	42	48	52	58	65	69	66	61	54	35	29	53
Grand Rapids	56	26	37	48	54	60	66	72	67	58	50	31	22	49
Marquette	55	31	40	47	52	53	56	63	57	47	38	24	24	47
S. Ste. Marie	60	28	44	50	54	54	59	63	58	45	36	21	22	47
Minn. Duluth	49	47	55	60	58	58	60	68	63	53	47	36	40	55
Minneapolis	45	49	54	55	57	60	64	72	69	60	54	40	40	56
Miss. Vicksburg	66	46	50	57	64	69	73	69	72	74	71	60	45	64
Mo. Kansas City	69	55	57	59	60	64	70	76	73	70	67	59	52	65
St. Louis	68	48	49	56	59	64	68	72	68	67	65	54	44	61
Springfield	45	48	54	57	60	63	69	77	72	71	65	58	48	63
Mont. Havre	55	49	58	61	63	63	65	78	75	64	57	48	46	62
Helena	65	46	55	58	60	59	63	77	74	63	57	48	43	60
Kalispell	50	28	40	49	57	58	60	77	73	61	50	28	20	53
Nebr. Lincoln	55	57	59	60	60	63	69	76	71	67	66	59	55	64
North Platte	53	63	63	64	62	64	72	78	74	72	70	62	58	68
Nev. Ely	21	61	64	68	65	67	79	79	81	81	73	67	62	72
Las Vegas	19	74	77	78	81	85	91	84	86	92	84	83	75	82
Reno	51	59	64	69	75	77	82	90	89	86	76	68	56	76
Winnemucca	53	52	60	64	70	76	83	90	90	86	75	62	53	74
N.H. Concord	44	48	53	55	53	51	56	57	58	55	50	43	43	52

Mean Percentage of Possible Sunshine for Selected Locations *(Cont.)*

State and Station	Years	Jan.	Feb.	Mar.	Apr.	May	June	July	Aug.	Sept.	Oct.	Nov.	Dec.	Annual
N.J. Atlantic City	62	51	57	58	59	62	65	67	66	65	54	58	52	60
N. Mex. Albuquerque	28	70	72	72	76	79	84	76	75	81	80	79	70	76
Roswell	47	69	72	75	77	76	80	76	75	74	74	74	69	74
N.Y. Albany	63	43	51	53	53	57	62	63	61	58	54	39	38	53
Binghamton	63	31	39	41	44	50	56	54	51	47	43	29	26	44
Buffalo	49	32	41	49	51	59	67	70	67	60	51	31	28	53
Canton	43	37	47	50	48	54	61	63	61	54	45	30	31	49
New York	83	49	56	57	59	62	65	66	64	64	61	53	50	59
Syracuse	49	31	38	45	50	58	64	67	63	56	47	29	26	50
N.C. Asheville	57	48	53	56	61	64	63	59	59	62	64	59	48	58
Raleigh	61	50	56	59	64	67	65	62	62	63	64	62	52	61
N. Dak. Bismarck	65	52	58	56	57	58	61	73	69	62	59	49	48	59
Devils Lake	55	53	60	59	60	59	62	71	67	59	56	44	45	58
Fargo	39	47	55	56	58	62	63	73	69	60	57	39	46	59
Williston	43	51	59	60	63	66	66	78	75	65	60	48	48	63
Ohio Cincinnati	44	41	46	52	56	62	69	72	68	68	60	46	39	57
Cleveland	65	29	36	45	52	61	67	71	68	62	54	32	25	50
Columbus	65	36	44	49	54	63	68	71	68	66	60	44	35	55
Okla. Oklahoma City	62	57	60	63	64	65	74	78	78	74	68	64	57	68
Oreg. Baker	46	41	49	56	61	63	67	83	81	74	62	46	37	60
Portland	69	27	34	41	49	52	55	70	65	55	42	28	23	48
Roseburg	29	24	32	40	51	57	59	79	77	68	42	28	18	51
Pa. Harrisburg	60	43	52	55	57	61	65	68	63	62	58	47	43	57
Philadelphia	66	45	56	57	58	61	62	64	61	62	61	53	49	57
Pittsburgh	63	32	39	45	50	57	62	64	61	62	54	39	30	51
R.I. Block Island	48	45	54	47	56	58	60	62	62	60	59	50	44	56
S.C. Charleston	61	58	60	65	72	73	70	66	66	67	68	68	57	66
Columbia	55	53	57	62	68	69	68	63	65	64	68	64	51	63
S. Dak. Huron	62	55	62	60	62	65	68	76	72	66	61	52	49	63
Rapid City	53	58	62	63	62	61	66	73	73	69	66	58	54	64
Tenn. Knoxville	62	42	49	53	59	64	66	64	59	64	64	53	41	57
Memphis	55	44	51	57	64	68	74	73	74	70	69	58	45	64
Nashville	63	42	47	54	60	65	69	69	68	69	65	55	42	59
Tex. Abilene	14	64	68	73	66	73	86	83	85	73	71	72	66	73
Amarillo	54	71	71	75	75	75	82	81	81	79	76	76	70	76
Tex. Austin	33	46	50	57	60	62	72	76	79	70	70	57	49	63
Brownsville	37	44	49	51	57	65	73	78	78	67	70	54	44	61
Del Rio	36	53	55	61	63	60	66	75	80	69	66	58	52	63
El Paso	53	74	77	81	85	87	87	78	78	80	82	80	73	80
Ft. Worth	33	56	57	65	66	67	75	78	78	74	70	63	58	68
Galveston	66	50	50	55	61	69	76	72	71	70	74	62	49	63
San Antonio	57	48	51	56	58	60	69	74	75	69	67	55	49	62

Mean Percentage of Possible Sunshine for Selected Locations *(Cont.)*

State and Station	Years	Jan.	Feb.	Mar.	Apr.	May	June	July	Aug.	Sept.	Oct.	Nov.	Dec.	Annual
Utah Salt Lake City	22	48	53	61	68	73	78	82	82	84	73	56	49	69
Vt. Burlington	54	34	43	48	47	53	59	62	59	51	43	25	24	46
Va. Norfolk	60	50	57	60	63	67	66	66	66	63	64	60	51	62
Richmond	56	49	55	59	63	67	66	65	62	63	64	58	50	61
Wash. North Head	44	28	37	42	48	48	48	50	46	48	41	31	27	41
Seattle	26	27	34	42	48	53	48	62	56	53	36	28	24	45
Spokane	62	26	41	53	63	64	68	82	79	68	53	28	22	58
Tatoosh Island	49	26	36	39	45	47	46	48	44	47	38	26	23	40
Walla Walla	44	24	35	51	63	67	72	86	84	72	59	33	20	60
Yakima	18	34	49	62	70	72	74	86	86	74	61	38	29	65
W. Va. Elkins	55	33	37	42	47	55	55	56	53	55	51	41	33	48
Parkersburg	62	30	36	42	49	56	60	63	60	60	53	37	29	48
Wis. Green Bay	57	44	51	55	56	58	64	70	65	58	52	40	40	55
Madison	59	44	49	52	53	58	64	70	66	60	56	41	38	56
Milwaukee	59	44	48	53	56	60	65	73	67	62	56	44	39	57
Wyo. Cheyenne	63	65	66	64	61	59	68	70	68	69	69	65	63	66
Lander	57	66	70	71	66	65	74	76	75	72	67	61	62	69
Sheridan	52	56	61	62	61	61	67	76	74	67	60	53	52	64
Yellowstone Park	35	39	51	55	57	56	63	73	71	65	57	45	38	56
P.R. San Juan	57	64	69	71	66	59	62	65	67	61	63	63	65	65

Based on period of record through December 1959, except in a few instances.

GLOSSARY

Absorber plate. In a flat-plate collector the surface that absorbs heat from the sun and transfers it to air or a fluid medium flowing across it.

Absorptance. The ratio of energy absorbed by a surface to the energy striking it. Black, low-gloss surfaces have high absorptances; white or shiny metal surfaces have low absorptances.

Absorption chiller. An air conditioning device in which the refrigerant is absorbed into a water solution, and out of which the refrigerant is evaporated by solar heat.

Active solar system. A solar water or space heating system that collects, stores, and distributes the sun's heat by means of mechanical devices such as pumps or blowers.

Berm. A mass of earth banked around a house, particularly at the northern exposure. The object is to insulate the dwelling and protect it from cold winds.

British thermal unit (Btu). The amount of heat energy required to raise one pound (one pint) of water 1 degree F; the standard means of measuring the heating requirements of homes and the output of heat-producing devices.

Closed loop. A type of solar space or hot water heating system in which the fluid circulating through the collectors does not come in direct contact with the water in storage, but exchanges heat through the surface of a coil in a tank.

Collector efficiency. The ratio of usable heat energy extracted from a solar collector to the solar energy striking the collector.

Collector tilt. The angle, measured from the horizontal, at which a solar collector is tilted to face the sun.

Concentrating collector. A solar collector in which the sun's heat energy is focused, or concentrated, onto a tube through which a liquid flows. A liquid so heated can attain much higher temperatures than if it were circulated through an ordinary flat-plate collector.

Convection. Heat carried from one surface to another by moving currents of air.

Degree day. A measurement used in determining heating and cooling requirements. The total degree days for a given day is equal to the difference, in degrees Fahrenheit, between the day's average temperature and 65°F. Thus, a day with an average temperature of 20°F would have 45 degree days.

Design temperature. The lowest anticipated temperature for a given climatic area; used in calculating the heat load of a house.

Direct gain. Heat energy which is received from the sun at the point where it is needed; in simplest terms, it is represented by sunshine coming through a window.

Domestic hot water. The heated water supplies drawn by tap and used for baths, showers, and cleaning. Not to be confused with the water in a hydronic space heating system.

Drainback. A solar collection and storage system in which the heat-absorbing water drains into storage after the winter sun goes down, a precaution against freezing damage to collectors.

Draindown. Similar to the above, with the difference that the water drains into a sump rather than into the system's main storage tank.

Emittance. The measure of the heat reradiated from a solar collector's absorber plate.

Eutectic salts. A family of substances that melt at low temperatures (90–120°F) and that can release heat as they resolidify. Used for heat storage in some air-type solar heating systems.

Evacuated tube collector. A solar collector in which the heat exchange fluid circulates through tubes surrounded by vacuum space; used for high-temperature applications.

Flat-plate collector. A device in which the sun's energy is absorbed and used to heat an exchange medium; the standard collector for domestic space and hot water heating.

Heat load. The heating requirements of a house, generally expressed in terms of the amount of Btu that escape per hour through its surfaces.

Heat pump. A device that, by extracting heat from one substance or environment and delivering it to another, is able to provide both heat and air conditioning.

Heat sink. A substance into which heat has been transferred; it is then capable of holding and slowly releasing this heat.

Heat source. A substance capable of transferring heat to another, cooler substance; in heat pump terminology, the object or environment from which heat is extracted for delivery to a *heat sink* elsewhere (see above).

Heat transfer. The process by which heat travels from a warmer to a cooler substance or environment. Heat always flows in this direction, with the result being an equalization of temperatures between the two substances.

Hybrid. A house that incorporates both active and passive solar technology.

Hydronic system. A home heating system in which hot water or steam circulates through a series of radiators or convectors.

Indirect gain. Heat energy received from the sun in one location and transferred, via passive means, to where it is needed. The Trombe wall is an adaptation of the indirect gain principle.

Insolation. The amount of solar radiation received in a given area over a prescribed length of time; shortened form of *Incident solar radiation*.

Langley. The basic unit of insolation measurement. A langley equals one calorie of radiant energy per square centimeter, or 3.69 Btu per square foot.

Life-cycle costing. The procedure of calculating the total cost of a solar installation over its estimated lifetime.

Passive solar system. Any construction feature or combination of features designed to take advantage of the sun's energy without the use of mechanical equipment.

Payback period. The time over which a solar heating or domestic hot water system pays for itself in savings on conventional fuels.

Percentage of possible sunshine. For any area the percentage of time during which the sun can be expected to be strong enough to outline objects in shadow.

Photovoltaic. A process in which solar energy is converted into electricity, generally by means of a series of silicon discs called *photovoltaic cells.*

Pool cover. A plastic sheet placed over a solar-heated swimming pool in order to conserve heat. Under proper conditions some covers can allow pool heating via direct gain of solar energy.

Propylene glycol. A nontoxic antifreeze fluid which, when diluted in water, is used as the heat exchange medium in many closed-loop solar systems.

R value. The measurement of the heat-resisting ability of building and insulating materials.

Radiation. Along with convection and conduction, one of the three ways in which heat travels. Any object warmer than its surroundings radiates heat waves.

Re-radiation. The heat emitted by a warm collector plate to its cooler surroundings.

Retrofit. To retrofit a house is to make alterations or add equipment designed to improve the building's energy efficiency.

Selective surface. A special coating, commonly black chrome on a nickel backing, applied to the absorber plate in a solar collector, the object being to absorb as much and re-radiate as little solar energy as possible.

Site-built collectors. Collectors that are assembled at the location where they are to be used, often as an integral part of the structure they will heat. The alternative, installation of factory built collectors, can be expensive if a large array is required.

Solar access. Often referred to as "sun rights." A growing area of legal interpretation, concerned with the rights of solar home owners to unobstructed sunlight.

Solar tracking. The mechanical adjustment of solar collectors so that they constantly receive maximum sunlight. Generally employed only with *concentrating collectors* (see above).

Stack effect. In home ventilation the tendency of air to evacuate through openings on upper levels as heated air masses rise.

Temperature difference. The difference between the *design temperature* and the desired indoor temperature of a house; used in calculating the *heat load* of the house.

Thermal mass. The ability of an object to store heat. Also used to designate building materials, such as masonry or stone, used in passive solar homes because of their ability to release stored heat slowly and steadily.

Thermal resistance. The ability of a material to resist the flow of heat.

Thermosiphon. Any of a number of solar systems that rely on the natural buoyancy of heated air or water, rather than mechanical equipment, to move heat from where it is collected to where it is needed.

Trombe wall. A passive indirect gain system invented by Dr. Felix Trombe. Actually two walls—one masonry, one glass—it provides both thermal mass and the ability to cycle heated air into a room.

Tube-in-plate collector. A collector in which water or antifreeze is circulated through tubing that lies within the plate itself, rather than above or below it.

BIBLIOGRAPHY

Alves, Ronald and Milligan, Charles. *Living with Energy*. New York: Penguin Books, 1978.

Anderson, Bruce. *Solar Energy: Fundamentals in Building Design*. New York: McGraw-Hill, 1977.

Anderson, Bruce, and Riordan, Michael. *The Solar Home Book*. Harrisville, NH: Cheshire Books, 1976.

Cinquemani, V., Owenby, J. R., and Baldwin, R. G. *Input Data for Solar Systems*. Washington: Prepared for U. S. Department of Energy, 1978.

Clegg, Peter, and Watkins, Derry. *The Complete Greenhouse Book*. Charlotte, VT: Garden Way publishing, 1978.

Commoner, Barry. *The Politics of Energy*. New York: Knopf, 1979.

Daniels, George. *Solar Homes and Sun Heating*. New York: Harper and Row, 1976.

Foster, Ruth S. *Homeowner's Guide to Landscaping That Saves Energy Dollars*. New York: David McKay, 1978.

Hayes, Denis. *Rays of Hope: The Transition to a Post-Petroleum World*. New York: Norton, 1977.

Keyes, John H. *Consumer Handbook of Solar Energy*. Dobbs Ferry, NY: Earth Books/Morgan & Morgan, 1979.

Leckie, Jim, and others. *Other Homes and Garbage: Designs for Self-Sufficient Living*. San Francisco: Sierra Club Books, 1975.

Lucas, Ted. *How to Build a Solar Heater*. Pasadena: Ward Ritchie Press, 1975.

Mazria, Edward. *The Passive Solar Energy Book*. Emmaus, PA: Rodale Press, 1979.

Olgyay, Victor. *Design with Climate*. Princeton, NJ: Princeton University Press, 1973.

Performance Testing of a Residential Solar Climate Control System Using a Water Trickle Collector and a Water-Rockbed Thermal Storage During a Winter Period. Washington, D.C.: National Technical Information Service, 1979.

Scheller, William. *Energy-Saving Home Improvements*. Indianapolis: Howard W. Sams, 1979.

Sunset Homeowner's Guide to Solar Heating. San Francisco: Lane Publishing Co., 1978.

Wright, David. *Natural Solar Architecture: A Passive Primer*. New York: Van Nostrand Reinhold, 1978.

INDEX

Absorber plates, 24, 26, 28, 42, 47, 57, 61, 71, 73, 74, 97, 109, 119
  bonding of, 27-28
"Absorption chiller," 108-109
Air-conditioning, 15, 66, 67, 71, 102, 104, 122, 129, 131
Air-conditioning, solar, 8, 30, 70, 102, 106-109
Air flow: in air collectors, 74, 79, 83-84
Altitude, solar, 16, 113
Aluminum, 25, 26, 27, 29, 37
Angling of collectors, 15, 17, 29-30, 32, 35, 57, 91, 97, 98
Antifreeze, 7, 27, 41, 43-44, 57, 60, 61, 71, 72, 92
Appliances, household, 89, 127
Architecture: and passive solar systems, 8-10, 112, 113, 118-119, 123, 125-127
  and payback, 91
  and solar space heating, 53
Attics, 20, 139
Azimuth, 16, 113
Basements, 20, 75, 76
Berm house, 125
Blowers, 8-10, 73, 74, 79, 80, 81, 84, 85, 86, 92, 104
BTU's, 17, 32, 57, 59, 64, 67, 127, 132, 139
Building: inspection, 35, 44
  permits, 36
Caulking, 21, 38, 132
Cellulose, 20
Chimneys, 21
Closed loop systems, 41, 42-43, 57, 60, 92
Coal, 3, 56
Collectors, solar, 7, 10, 11, 15, 17, 23-24, 30, 42, 46, 47, 56, 57, 58, 59, 60, 61, 62, 64, 65, 83, 84, 91, 95, 101, 102, 103, 106, 108, 109, 112, 113, 119, 136, 137
Convection, 120, 122, 128, 135
Convectors, 55, 57, 58, 60, 61, 64
Doors, 20, 135
Drafts, 20, 120, 121, 123, 125
Drainback systems, 41-42, 43, 57, 60, 61, 72, 99, 108
Drapes, 124, 128
Ducts, 32, 35, 56, 64, 65, 80, 84, 86, 119, 121
  and solar collectors, 72, 73, 74, 76, 104, 113
Electricity, 17, 44, 47, 51, 63, 64, 70, 81, 89, 90, 91, 92, 93, 94, 103, 107, 108
Energy: conservation of, 51, 54, 81, 87, 90, 100, 127, 136
  shortage of, 3
Energy: solar, 3, 7-8, 11-17, 24
  measurement of, 16-17, 145-148
Eutectic salts, 81-82, 107
Evacuated tube collector, 109
Fans, 135
Fiberglass, 25, 28, 29, 48, 50, 58, 59, 78
Fiberglass batting, 20, 78
Fireplaces, 114
Flat-plate collectors, air, 24, 35, 71-87, 107
  and capacity of system, 82-84
  and domestic hot water, 84-85
  and solar cooling, 103-106, 109, 128
  and space heating, 85-87
  installation of, 72
  location of, 74, 76
  storage system for 73, 74, 75-82
Flat-plate collectors, liquid, 14, 15, 23-24, 26, 32, 57, 64, 83
  and capacity of system, 82-83, 90
  components of 25-28
  efficiency of, 57
  installation of 23, 28, 35-40, 104
  location of, 29-33
Fossil fuels, 3, 9, 57, 64, 89, 90, 92, 93
Furnaces, 50, 56, 57, 64, 65, 67, 71, 80, 86, 93, 121, 129
  electric, 50, 56, 63, 70, 86

wood, 55, 56
Gas, 3, 17, 56, 86, 91
Gaskets, 28
Gauges, 50
Glauber's salt, 81-82
Glazing, 7, 24, 26, 28, 29, 74, 96, 109, 112, 116, 119, 123, 131, 132, 135
Greenhouses, solar, 9, 112, 131-136
and energy savings, 132, 135-136
design of, 132-135
thermal storage of, 134-135
"Greenhouse effect," 24, 101, 120, 132
Heat-exchange coil, 7, 42, 43, 44, 46, 47, 50, 60, 61, 65, 70, 80, 84, 86, 108
Heat load, 59, 63, 83, 91, 127
calculation of, 139-140
Heat pumps, 56, 66-71, 87, 102, 106, 107
and solar energy, 70-71
and solar-heated swimming pools, 102
efficiency of, 47, 67, 70
models of, 70
Heat sink, 67, 102
Heating, steam, 56
Heating systems, electric, 56, 63, 71, 94
efficiency of, 63-64
radiant, 63, 64
Heating systems: forced air, 56, 58, 64-65, 70, 71, 73, 80, 86
gas, 50, 56, 63, 89, 91, 93
hot water, 56, 60, 61, 84, 91, 92
oil, 50, 56, 63, 89, 91, 93
Hot water tanks: and solar heating, 65
Humidifiers, 73
"Hybrid systems," 8, 54, 136-137
Inflation, 90, 94
Insolation, 16-17, 91
Insulation, 15, 19-21, 28, 32, 40, 47, 54, 55, 58, 59, 74, 76, 78, 84, 85, 90, 91, 96, 113, 122, 123, 124-125, 127, 128, 132, 134, 135, 137, 139
Landscaping, 32, 53, 125, 128
"Langleys," 17
Latitude, 15, 17, 29, 30, 97, 98
"Life-cycle costing," 92
Manifolds: in air systems, 35, 74
in liquid systems, 40
Masonry, 8, 78, 114, 115, 116, 118, 119, 135
Meter, flow, 51
Meter, watt-hour, 50
"Microclimate," 125, 127, 128
Mixing valve, 50
National Energy Act, 93
Paraffin, 82
"Payback," 10, 20, 25, 49, 53, 56, 83, 89, 93-94, 95, 136
calculation of, 90-93
Plastics, 26, 28, 59, 97
Plumbing, 35, 41, 42, 48, 56, 58, 64
and solar collectors, 72
Polystyrene, 20
Polyurethane, 59
Pressure relief valve, 40
Pumps, 8, 10, 41, 44-47, 51, 60, 61, 92, 100, 108, 109
Radiation: solar, 11, 14, 15, 16, 17, 24, 120, 121, 125
diffuse, 14, 17
direct, 14
Radiators, 54, 56, 57, 60, 61, 64, 119
"R value," 20, 28, 59, 122, 139, 140
Refrigerants, 67, 107, 108, 109
Registers, 64, 65, 80
Resistance, 20, 63
"Retrofit," 54, 91
"Roof ponds," 130-131
Roofs, 7, 19, 20, 42, 53, 128, 130, 131, 132
and installation of collectors, 35-40
and location of collectors, 30-32
Septic tanks: as storage tanks, 59
Shades, 16, 124, 128
Shading, 32, 54, 128, 137
Shutters, 124, 128, 129, 132
Skylights, 7, 116, 131
Snow, 132
"SolaRoll," 28-29, 74
Solar conversion, feasibility of, 7-8, 54-56, 71
incentives for, 93, 94
Solar cooling, 17, 103-110, 111, 121, 122
Solar heating: hot water, 3, 7, 8, 14, 15, 17, 20, 24, 30, 37, 42, 44, 49, 50, 53, 54, 57, 61, 64, 65, 80, 84, 85, 89, 90, 92, 93, 94, 95, 106, 137
space heating, 7, 8, 14, 15, 17, 24, 26, 30, 37, 42, 53-71, 74, 80, 84, 85, 89, 90, 93, 95, 97, 106, 137
Solar systems: active, 8, 10, 11, 14, 17, 20, 63, 89, 92, 103, 106, 113, 136-137
installation of, 35-40
selection of, 53-56, 82-84
manufacturers of, 141-143
passive, 3, 8-10, 11, 14, 15, 20, 54, 136-137
and cooling, 128-131
and heat conservation, 122-127
and thermal storage, 114-116, 119, 122
and water storage, 116-118, 119, 121, 129
design of, 111-113, 118-119, 122, 125, 128
location of, 125-127
Space heaters, 56, 57, 64
"Stack effect," 106
Stone, 114, 119
Storage bins, liquid, 80-81
Storage bins, rock, 71, 73, 75, 76, 83, 84, 86, 87, 99, 103-104, 135
components of, 76-80
size of, 78, 81, 82-83, 86, 90
Storage tanks, solar, 10, 15, 32, 41, 42, 44, 46, 47, 49-50, 56, 58, 59, 61, 62, 64, 65, 70, 83, 99, 102, 108, 113

insulation of, 48-49
prefabricated, 58-59
selection of, 57
site-built, 58-59
size of, 47-48, 59, 63, 65, 83
Stoves, wood, 8, 55, 56, 64, 86, 115
Stress, structural, 35
Styrofoam, 59
in solar greenhouses, 132, 134, 135
Sumps, 41
Sun chart, 113
"Sun rights," 33
Swimming pools, solar heating of, 70, 95-102
and heat conservation, 100-101
and heat pumps, 99, 100-101
collectors for, 96-99
location of, 97-98
operation of, 99-100
Thermal mass, 85, 129, 135
Thermal storage,
and passive solar systems, 113-118, 122
in solar greenhouses, 132, 134-136
"Thermistor," 46
Thermometers, 41, 50
Thermostats, 42, 47, 50, 61, 63, 64, 65, 85, 86, 115
Trombe wall, 119-121, 135
and cooling function, 121, 128
Tubing, 26, 28, 42, 74, 97
bonding of, 27-28
Urethane foam, 28
Vents, 60, 121, 135
Ventilation, 128, 135, 137
Walls, 19, 20, 75, 115, 125, 130, 132, 135
Water heaters,
electric, 94
gas, 50, 89
Weather stripping, 21, 54, 90
Wind, 26, 35, 36, 54, 100, 127, 128
and saltbox design, 125
Windows, 3, 16, 20, 112, 113, 114, 115, 116, 119, 122, 124, 125, 128, 129, 130, 135, 137
clerestory, 116
storm, 54
Wood, 25, 59, 78
Zoning, 33